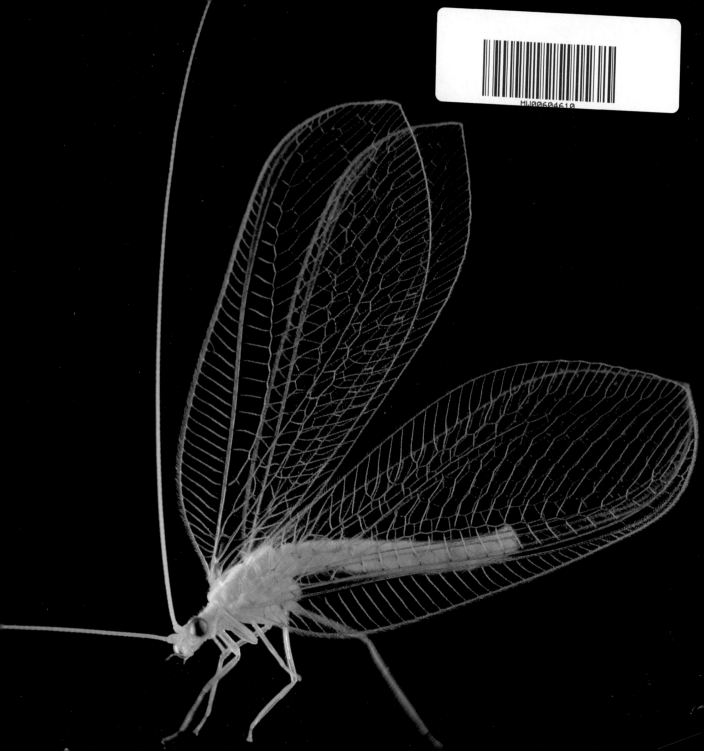

WAO AKUA

SACRED SOURCE OF LIFE

DIVISION OF FORESTRY AND WILDLIFE
DEPARTMENT OF LAND AND NATURAL RESOURCES
STATE OF HAWAI'I

CONTENTS

Featuring
photographs by:

David Liittschwager &
  Susan Middleton
Jack Jeffrey
Franco Salmoiraghi
Kapulani Landgraf
Richard A. Cooke III
Masako Cordray
Frans Lanting
Jan Becket
Shuzo Uemoto
Hal Lum
Maya L. Legrande

Acknowledgments, permissions, and editorial and copyright information appear on pages 131–134.

FOREWORD THINK MAUKA

Sam ʻOhukaniʻōhiʻa Gon III

The State Legislature designated 2003 as "The Year of the Hawaiian Forest"—twelve months in which to celebrate the centennial of the forest reserve system in Hawaiʻi and to redouble efforts to steward the Islands' extraordinary forest legacy.

Hawaiʻi's forest reserve system was created by the Territorial Legislature in 1903, at the urging of foresters and sugar growers concerned about watershed health. It was among the first such protected watersheds in the United States. The timing was critical: after a century of logging and grazing by cattle, feral pigs, goats, and sheep, the forests had been greatly diminished. For example, over 90 percent of Oʻahu's lowland forests had been lost.

With a little thought, it becomes plain how much we owe to the ecosystem services that Hawaiian woodlands provide: we pay no bill for the clean water constantly replenishing island aquifers, no bill for natural erosion control and clear near-shore waters. We pay no bill for the uptake of carbon dioxide and the supply of oxygen, for the calming influence of green mountains on our psyche, or for the shady trails we hike. We tend to take it all for granted, but the Year of the Hawaiian Forest will allow us all to review just how close we came to letting it all be destroyed a hundred years ago.

During 2003, the state Department of Land and Natural Resources (and especially the Division of Forestry and Wildlife) held events and programs designed to showcase Hawaiʻi's diversity of forest types, which are far richer than the koa or ʻōhiʻa forests that most people think about (if they think *mauka* at all)—from the spectacular remnant *hala* forests along windward coasts to high-elevation *māmane* forests on desolate, sub-alpine cinder slopes a thousand feet above the clouds; from Kauaʻi's mist-shrouded swamp forests of dwarf ʻōhiʻa and *lapalapa*, to the dry forests of *lama* and *olopua*, on the arid leeward slopes of Lānaʻi.

Some of our native forests are so rich in tree species that they defy naming. Scientists are forced to refer to them as "diverse mesic forests" because the list of constituent trees is so long and the mix so evenly blended that none of the species can be called dominant.

opposite

Cyrtandra paliku

The Hawaiian name for this perennial herb covered with reddish black hairs means vertical cliff. This hints at its success and also its vulnerability. On the island of Kauaʻi it was discovered clinging precariously to a steep cliff face. It is protected from most alien weed species that might threaten its survival, and yet for this very rare Cyrtandra paliku *the primary threat is the not so rare rockslide.* Photo by David Liittschwager and Susan Middleton

Few people realize that the Hawaiian archipelago's number of classifiable forest types is so high. The national vegetation standard, used to describe floristics across the United States, counts no less than 48 native Hawaiian forest and woodland types, within which live over 175 species of native Hawaiian trees. Almost none of these is found anywhere else on Earth.

These are the forests that saw to the material-culture needs of ancient Hawai'i, from the brilliant feathers of forest birds to the hardest woods of the farmer and the warrior—woods such as *uhiuhi*, so dense as to sink in water.

The forests saw to (and still see to) Hawaiian spiritual needs as well: the uplands are the *wao akua*, or the realm of the gods, sacred to Kū, the god of war, governance, and leadership. When a large *'ōhi'a* tree was felled for ritual purposes, a human sacrifice was demanded, so high was the *mana* of the tree. Forests also feed the spirits of artists and healing practitioners. Laka, the goddess of hula, is a forest-dweller, and the herbal healers, who gathered from the sacred forests, prayed to Kū and his wife Hina before selecting herbs for curing ailments of and restoring balance within their patients.

And, like patients in a hospital, the health of our forests ranges from reasonably secure (think of the tens of thousands of acres of relatively intact wet *'ōhi'a* forest on the island of Hawai'i) to hanging onto existence by a thread (as in the last stands of dry forest in the Wai'anae Mountains).

The next century of forest stewardship may see restoration of some of these valuable, rare native forests, or, like so many fragile and wonderful things, they may be swept away. The Year of the Hawaiian Forest, 2003, was a starting point.

INTRODUCTION ❦ RAINS ALWAYS FOLLOW THE FOREST
Michael G. Buck

I have been privileged to work for the Hawai'i Department of Land and Natural Resources for over a quarter century, and I am honored to have been in charge of its Forestry and Wildlife Division for over a decade. The division has stewardship responsibilities for over 800,000 acres of Hawai'i's public forests and the wildlife that lives there. My life has become intertwined with the history of Hawai'i's forests. I think I see forest issues clearer than most, for I have experienced almost all of Hawai'i's forests and am a student of their history. Like Sir Isaac Newton, I have been standing on the shoulders of giants. I have been blessed.

A century ago, with incredible foresight and vision, public and private interests came together to protect and expand Hawai'i's forests, creating one of the nation's first forest reserve systems. The trees in Hawai'i's forests today, like the people in our state, have come from all over the world, forming new living communities that the Earth has never seen before. And like Hawai'i's native people, the forests are very special. We have inherited a treasure.

What Were the Forests Like for the First Children of Hawai'i?

The first children of Hawai'i, whose parents came here over 1,000 years ago, grew up on the world's most isolated archipelago, one with high mountains, a multitude of climates, abundant rainfall, and forests covering almost all of the lands, including the lowland areas. For tens of thousands of years before the first humans arrived, plants and animals had evolved together, forming native forest ecosystems of great beauty and diversity.

On their long discovery voyage, the parents of Hawai'i's first children brought new plants and animals with them, for food and medicinal use. The people quickly learned to use the native forest resources for clothing, medicine, shelter, and in their cultural practices. Their traditions reflect a close and long-standing relationship with the native forest. They celebrated the forest in chant, song, and dance, and its many gifts provided for the people's spiritual and material needs—water from the forest fed the *lo'i* (taro fields) in the lowlands and the *loko i'a* (fishponds) along the coast.

opposite

One of Hawai'i's unique ecosystems is found at the top of the West Maui mountains in Maui Land and Pineapple Company's Pu'u Kukui Preserve. The more porous lava of the volcano's caldera erodes after thousands of years leaving higher density lava remaining. This substrate creates a water-saturated ecosystem known as a bog.

Seen here is Silversword Bog at Pu'u Kukui with greenswords (Argyroxiphium grayanum) *in bloom and dwarf 'ōhi'a* (Metrosideros polymorpha) *in the foreground. Because of the high wind and cold conditions at higher elevations in Hawai'i, the hardy plants that live in these environments take on a reduced form, although they are full grown.*
Photo by David Liittschwager and Susan Middleton

They used the woods from the forest to make houses, canoes, weapons, and tools. They gathered forest plants and herbs for medicines and fashioned the feathers of birds into brilliantly colored capes, helmets, and lei.

Hawaiian society was based on the *ahupua'a* system of land management, which evolved to protect the upland water resources that sustained human life. A typical *ahupua'a* was wedge-shaped and extended from the mountains to the sea. The upland forest was *wao akua*, the realm of the gods, and the trees were a physical manifestation of this spiritual realm. Entry into the forest was limited to a few individuals. As water flowed from the upland forest, down through the *ahupua'a*, it passed from the *wao akua*, the realm of the gods, to the *wao kanaka*, the realm of man, where it sustained agriculture, aquaculture, and other human activities. Water was a gift from the gods, and Hawaiians understood the relationship between their forests and their survival. The ancient proverb sums it up—*Hahai nō ka ua i ka ulu lā'au* (Rains always follow the forest).

The first people to come to Hawai'i, and all those who followed, have altered the natural ecosystems. Long before European contact with Hawai'i, large stretches of dry, lowland forests were cleared, primarily by fire, in slash-and-burn agriculture. By approximately 1600, the Hawaiian population had grown so large that settlements encroached ever further into forested areas. When Captain James Cook visited the Hawaiian Islands in 1778, he observed that the forests began at middle elevations, a considerable distance from the coast. A vast area of grassland stretched from his anchorage at Waimea Bay, Kaua'i, to the inland forest belt: "not even a shrub grows naturally on this extensive space," he noted.

Environmental change accelerated after Western contact. Cook introduced the goat to Hawai'i; Vancouver brought cattle and sheep. Protected by a royal *kapu* (taboo), grazing animals multiplied rapidly. In 1833, the naturalist David Douglas noted that "the grassy flanks of the mountain [Mauna Kea] abound with wild cattle, the offspring of the stock left here by Captain Vancouver." Although the *kapu* had been lifted by that time—allowing commoners to kill cattle, sheep, and goats to supplement their food supplies—the number of herbivores continued to increase, and the environmental damage they caused was soon obvious. Shallow-rooting native species, in particular, suffered from the hooves of grazing ungulates, and slow-growing plant species recovered with difficulty when they were heavily browsed.

Buck

Moreover, as large populations of feral animals spread *mauka*, onto the steep slopes, the resulting erosion multiplied the adverse effects on the land.

Human incursion into the uplands brought more destruction. As early as 1790, the harvesting of sandalwood had become a major undertaking, and from 1815 to 1826, was at fever pitch. King Kamehameha I placed a *kapu* on the cutting of young sandalwood trees, hoping to conserve this valuable source of wealth. His successor, Liholiho, was less cautious, however, and granted harvesting privileges to various high chiefs, who gathered the sandalwood with abandon. Within two decades, the slow-growing sandalwood was virtually exterminated in the Islands. In 1839, when a law was finally passed restricting the cutting of sandalwood (the first forestry law in Hawai'i), it was already too late to save more than a few scattered mature trees.

By the late 1880s, people in the Islands were becoming acutely aware of one of the most serious consequences of forest depredation: the diminishing supply of high quality fresh water. Previously, the forests had protected the watershed by catching rain, allowing it to be absorbed into the aquifer while also feeding the streams. Depredation of the forest—and therefore the watershed—was occurring at the same time that both the urban population and the large-scale sugar industry were expanding. Demand for water began to outstrip the supply. For example, Honolulu's main source of water, Nu'uanu Stream, had become intermittent and undependable as a result of damage to the *mauka* forests caused by feral and domestic herbivores.

In response, the legislature of 1876 appropriated $25,000 for a new, larger reservoir to be built. The legislature also passed "An Act for the Protection and Preservation of Woods and Forests," authorizing the Minister of the Interior to set aside and protect woods and forest lands that were valuable either as watersheds or as sources of timber, and to appoint a superintendent of woods and forests to administer the resulting reservations.

In October 1882, *Planters' Monthly* published an essay that asked, "Who, that has lived here for twenty-five years or even less, has not observed the immense destruction that has taken place in our limited forests?" Just two years earlier, according to the essay, Makiki, Mānoa, and Nu'uanu valleys had all been "hidden beneath a wealth of richest vegetation," and the stream flow from them had been pure and constant. Now water came in occasional, destructive, muddy torrents, for the "valleys and

hillsides were almost wholly denuded of trees." Conditions were no better in the outer islands. Rains still followed the forests, but the forests were disappearing.

Like the sugar plantations, cattle ranching was also expanding, largely to feed the growing population that had been attracted by the sugar boom. This expansion, too, put great strain on the forests. At mid-century, ranching operations began near Honuaʻula, Maui. Thirty years later, observers reported that "the forest has retired far up the mountain," with timber commencing some 26 miles above where it had formerly begun. Moreover, as cattle ranching increased, pressure grew for the government to sell or lease forest lands under its control. The temptation to do so was great, for sales and leases offered a ready source of funds, which the government desperately needed.

Cattlemen recognized that they were contributing to deforestation while at the same time they were being hurt by it. Water sources that their herds depended upon were drying up, and they had to go ever farther into the mountains to find adequate supplies. In Kohala, the mountain had been deforested to the very top. But cattlemen balked at the expense of the fences needed to solve the problem. The trustees for the huge Parker Ranch did finally agree to cooperate in a fence-building program in the Hāmākua District of Hawaiʻi, but like other cattle interests they failed to add their voices to the growing cry for protection of the forests.

It was left to the sugar interests and their Honolulu allies to provide leadership in the drive for forest conservation. The Hawaiian Sugar Planters' Association, founded in 1895, formed a three-man forestry committee to investigate conditions and recommend appropriate legislation. In 1902, heeding calls from the association, Sanford B. Dole, a long-time supporter of forestry and the first territorial governor of the Islands, appointed local planters to serve as his agents in designating forest reserves in the Kohala, Hāmākua, and North Hilo districts of the island of Hawaiʻi. Dole also sent urgent requests to Washington, D.C., for a forester to come to survey the Territory's forests.

The Establishment of Hawaiʻi's Forest Reserve System
After his inspection tours of the Islands in 1902, Edward M. Griffith, an assistant forester with the United States Bureau of Forestry, said, "Forest protection means not only increasing the rainfall, but more important still, conserving the water

supply. The future welfare and agricultural prosperity of the Hawaiian Islands depends upon the preservation of the forest." When the legislature met early in 1903, a package of proposed forestry legislation was ready for consideration. The governor's agents pushed ahead with their work on the Big Island, hammering out consensus and building local support.

Sanford Dole's forestry proposals passed through the legislature largely unscathed. Act 44, approved by the Territorial Legislature on April 25, 1903, created Hawai'i's forest reserve system and sparked the largest public-private conservation partnership in the history of the state. Ralph S. Hosmer was Hawai'i's first Superintendent of Forestry, charged with creating Hawai'i's forest reserve system. In his 1911 address to the Board of Commissioners of Agriculture and Forestry, Hosmer said,

The time has come when to make the most of our Hawaiian forests, there is demanded the active cooperation of all forest owners. It is not enough merely to pass resolutions approving and applauding these forest projects. The time has come to put words into deeds. The purpose of conservation is so to use the natural resources that first and foremost we ourselves may derive the fullest benefit from them today, but also that we may then pass them on, unimpaired, so that those who come after us may continue to enjoy the same benefits. Let us, here in Hawaii, look to it, each person on their own land, but all working together to a common end, that every one is doing their part to conserve through wise use the most important of our natural resources, the forest and waters of Hawaii nei.

A significant turning point for Hosmer's efforts came in 1906, when Alexander & Baldwin gave to the Board of Agriculture and Forestry control of a vast area of forested watershed on Maui that the company had protected for seventeen years. Prior to this, most private owners had preferred to depend upon their own devices, rather than on the well-intentioned but under-funded efforts of the government. Now, many landowners followed Alexander & Baldwin's example. In exchange for surrendering their property to the Territory for purposes of watershed management, the owners retained the right to use the water and did not pay property tax.

During the first decade of the Territory's forest management program, thirty-seven forest reserves, totaling nearly 800,000 acres, were established. A primary goal of the new management program was the exclusion of wild livestock and

Buck

other feral animals from the native forests. To accomplish this, the Territory enlisted the help of the general public by issuing hunting licenses. The scale and scope of the results were unprecedented. Between 1921 and 1946, over 257,000 feral animals were removed from the forest on the island of Hawai'i alone: an average of more than 10,000 animals per year. Over 500 miles of fence were built, replaced, and repaired. Along with the fencing and elimination of feral livestock, tree planting and fire control programs were put in place. Although reforestation efforts had begun in the valleys behind Honolulu before 1900, after the creation of the forest reserve program approximately 400,000 trees per year were being planted. From 1935 to 1941, when the Civilian Conservation Corps was active in Hawai'i, an average of nearly two million trees were planted annually in the forest reserves.

Today we are all enjoying the benefits of these efforts on behalf of Hawai'i's forests. Hawai'i has the eleventh largest state-owned forest and natural area reserve system in the United States, and the nation's largest area of tropical rain forest. The forest reserves, along with much of the watershed within the conservation districts, are in good hydrologic condition. Hawai'i's long-standing policy of watershed protection has resulted in dramatic improvements from the degraded conditions that prevailed at the turn of the century. Former forest reserves are now national parks, wildlife refuges, Nature Conservancy preserves, and natural area reserves.

In spite of these achievements, however, much work is still needed. In recent years, public investment in watershed management has diminished at the same time that our community's demand for water resources has increased dramatically. Invasive weeds such as the dreaded miconia are taking over critical forested watersheds on Maui and Hawai'i. And if we stay on our present course, Hawai'i faces the possibility that it may run out of drinking water in the next twenty-five years. On O'ahu, this may happen even sooner. Yet Hawai'i spends less than one percent of the state budget to protect and manage the land and natural resources that are vital to our islands.

What has happened over the last 100 years that has caused us to lose sight of the value of watershed protection? As supplies of fresh water have diminished, debate over water use is getting louder and more litigious—but people are fighting over the faucet and ignoring where the water comes from. Instead of focusing on the natural system that is the source of all of our fresh water, most of the discussion revolves

around who owns the water and in which direction and on whose land it will flow.

Today, private landowners are reluctant to allow the state to manage their forested watersheds, as they no longer have any assurance or expectation that they will still be able to use the water provided from their lands. In addition, the counties have not encouraged landowners to allow public management of their forests by adopting real-property tax incentives to compensate them for the associated regulatory constraints and potential loss of market value. Restrictive conservation zoning has prevented development in watershed areas, but zoning by itself does not pay for watershed management.

As we wake to the dawn of the twenty-first century, the future of the Hawaiian forest is again in doubt, just as it was one hundred years ago. Today we are benefiting from the foresight of past investment in watershed management, but we are failing the children of the future if we do not ensure for them a dependable water supply. A decade of chronic budget shortfalls has left state forest managers struggling to sustain watersheds while at the same time dealing with the worst crisis of species extinction in the nation and the serious threats from alien plants and animals. If the Hawaiian forest is to survive for future generations, new public-private partnerships are needed now, just as they were needed a century ago.

If we want our children to see the forests in 2103, these are the five most important things that we need to do now:

1. Increase Dedicated Funding for Watershed Protection. Watershed partnerships are the most effective tool for long-term protection of Hawai'i's watersheds and native forest resources. These voluntary, cooperative partnerships enable public and private landowners to share their expertise and resources and jointly manage our watershed forests across ownership boundaries in the most efficient and cost-effective manner. The creation of the East Maui and West Maui Mountains Watershed Partnerships in 1991 and 1998 has reinvigorated the historic cooperative partnership of public and private sectors. In 1999, the Ko'olau Mountains Watershed Partnership, on the island of O'ahu, and an East Moloka'i Watershed Partnership were formed. The Ko'olau Mountains Watershed Partnership includes over 100,000 acres, with an estimated sustained yield of 135 billion gallons of fresh water annually. Recently, watershed partnerships for Lāna'i, Kaua'i, Kohala, and

Today, students begin learning at a young age how the forces acting in and upon the forests are delicately balanced. This winning poster is from the Year of the Hawaiian Forest children's poster contest (Mililani Mauka Elementary, 5th grade science club, spring 2003). Students based their posters on an activity that taught them about the complex relationships between plants and animals in an ecosystem.

South Maui have also been established. Today, nearly 300,000 acres of important watershed areas in Hawaiʻi have been placed within these unique public-private partnerships. If we expect landowners to make these kinds of long-term commitments of their lands and resources—which are necessary for the protection of a most precious public resource—then secure, dedicated public funding is essential.

2. Coordinate Statewide Leadership and Funding for Invasive Species Management. Invasive species of weeds, feral animals, alien insects, and diseases are the single greatest threat to the health and viability of Hawaiʻi's native forests and watersheds. The most cost-effective means of invasive species control is prevention. The cost and effort expended to control an invasive species once it has escaped into the wild is much higher than the cost of stopping it at ports of entry. Even when agencies and private organizations such as the invasive species committees are working together effectively, they still need increased funding for rapid response and control of invasive species such as miconia.

3. Support Public and Private Efforts to Restore Hawaiʻi's Native Koa Forests. Important native watershed forests are found on both public and private agriculturally zoned land on the islands of Hawaiʻi and Maui. Many of these forests, formerly dominated by koa, the monarch of the Hawaiian forest, are barely surviving after generations of harvesting, land clearing, and ranching. Removal of cattle and reforestation can restore many of these lands back into koa forests, providing ideal watersheds and habitats for native species, as well as sustainable commercial and cultural forest products.

4. Reconnect with Native Hawaiian Values that Support Forest Management. Management policy to preserve and enhance Hawaiʻi's forests should not ignore the traditional cultural component that affected those resources for 1,000 years or more prior to the establishment of the forest reserve system. If the stewardship and protection of Hawaiʻi's forests can incorporate the traditional Hawaiian component, model partnerships for management of cultural and natural resources can evolve to benefit forest resources for the long run. The East Molokaʻi Watershed Partnership embraces the concept of *ahupuaʻa* management and provides an example of how our watersheds can be managed to help sustain our island lifestyles. With

Buck

broad-based community support, this partnership is managing the upland forest to protect the island's primary source of fresh water, and in so doing is also reducing runoff and siltation in the farming and fishing communities below. This concept of *ahupuaʻa* management strengthens people's ties to the land and empowers local communities to protect their natural resources.

5. Increase Public Awareness and Involvement in Natural Resource Protection and Management. A healthy forest is no accident. Effective forest protection requires strong political and financial support and partnerships among public and private landowners. But support from the general public is also needed. The larger community is not sufficiently aware of what is at stake in the potential loss of the state's native forests and other ecosystems, or what community members can do to prevent this loss. Programs to develop environmental education curricula for Hawaiʻi schools should be expanded so that young people can learn about the Islands' watershed forests and native ecosystems, their struggle for survival, and the opportunities for saving them. University programs and more hands-on conservation experiences are essential to train conservation professionals for the future. Expanded public access and volunteer opportunities are also needed, to involve local communities in forest protection and management projects.

Am I optimistic about the future? Absolutely. In fact, I believe that Hawaiʻi can serve as a model for other states. History has already taught us the intimate connection between the forests and our quality of life. We are reminded of this connection every day as we see the summits of our forested mountains and swim in our nearshore waters. One hundred years ago, our society forged partnerships for the common good; such partnerships are even more important today—to protect our forests, native species, and watersheds. Crucial to such partnerships is our increasing capacity to embrace Hawaiian cultural values and to learn from them in our efforts to perpetuate the health of our forests.

While none of us will be around in 2103, our children will read about what we did in 2003. They might even read this book. I hope they do. May the forest be with us all.

overleaf

Silversword Bog, Puʻu Kukui Preserve.

Puʻu Kukui Preserve is part of a state-wide partnership program, unique in the country, incorporating privately held lands into a system of natural areas. The Natural Area Partnership Program offers assistance to private landowners whose land contains high quality native ecosystems. The land is placed under a conservation easement, which provides for the preservation of the land in perpetuity.

The land within Puʻu Kukui Preserve, owned by Maui Land and Pineapple Company, is being preserved with the help of the State of Hawaiʻi's Natural Area Partnership and the Nature Conservancy of Hawaiʻi.

Photo by David Liittschwager and Susan Middleton

Mauna Kea

*"The thread of ancestral memory
reminds us that the mountain,
like our parents, is the wellspring
and provider of physical and
spiritual nourishment."*
PUALANI KANAKA'OLE
KANAHELE

Photo by Franco Salmoiraghi

NATIVE HAWAIIAN ENVIRONMENT ૪ઢ

Pualani Kanakaʻole Kanahele

The popular interpretation of Mauna Kea is "white mountain." To the native Hawaiian, Mauna Kea is a *kūpuna*, ancestor, and an *one hānau*, birthplace. Therefore, it is not just a mountain mass, but something very personal. The following chant reveals the source of the name Mauna Kea.

> O hānau ka mauna a Wākea
> ʻŌpuʻu aʻe ka mauna a Kea
> ʻO Wākea ke kupuna kāne aliʻi
> ʻO Papawelinuʻu ke kupuna wahine
> Hānau kēlā lani koa lau a Hāloa
> Hānau ʻo Kawēkiu he ohi no ka moku
> Hānau ka mauna, He keiki mauna na Kea
> Kuamū ʻia e Kāne, Kuawa ʻia e Lono
> Hoʻi mai ʻo Wākea a loko o Lanimomoe
> Moe Wākea moe iā Papa,
> Hānau ka mauna he keiki kapu na Kea,
> ʻAe, ka mauna, hānau ka mauna.

> The mountain of Wākea is born
> The mountain Kea is budding upward
> Wākea is indeed the male ancestral chief
> Papawelinuʻu is the female ancestor
> That spreading branch of Hāloa is born
> Kawēkiu is born, a sprout for the island
> The mountain is born, A child mountain for Kea
> Rained upon by Kāne and grooved by Lono
> Wākea returns from Lanimomoe
> Wākea sleeps with Papa
> The mountain a chosen child for Kea is born
> The mountain, the mountain is born.

The mountain is afforded dignity and a sense of family by being named in honor of Wākea, or Sky Father. When considered as a namesake of Wākea, the mountain takes on that persona and, philosophically, acquires its deep roots and genealogy. This genealogy goes back to the "Wākea of time," or the beginning. Therefore the names Ka Mauna a Kea and Mauna Kea allow the sacred and common names to assimilate to one another, without forgetting either.

Lononuiākea was the original name for the island before that name was eventually usurped by the name Hawai'i. Lononuiākea is the sacred name of Lono, who is the god of stormy weather, dark clouds, and rain. Throughout Polynesia, only two islands were honored as "ka inoa akua," which literally means "having the names of gods." They are Lononuiākea-Hawai'i and Kanaloa, or Kaho'olawe. To our ancestors, then, these two islands were endowed with godly *mana*, as befitting their names.

According to our oral history, Hāmākua was a name given by Hawai'iloa to his youngest son. The *'āpana*, or land division, called Hāmākua encloses the very top of Mauna Kea and stretches to Mauna Loa. The *ahupua'a* named Ka'ohe is within Hāmākua and also encloses the very top of Mauna Kea and extends to Mauna Loa. The word Ka'ohe simply means "the bamboo." Bamboo was a vegetable manifestation of the primordial god Kāne and was used to carry water. Sometimes rainwater that became trapped in the upright green bamboo, and therefore had never touched the ground, was given as offering to the gods or used medicinally. Ka'ohe was perhaps also a description of the many riverbeds that time and erosion by water had carved through that section of Hāmākua.

Mauna Kea is also the *piko*, or navel, of the island, and this is another reason the mountain and the area around it is considered sacred. This *piko* generated the landmass of Hawai'i *mokupuni*. In addition, Hawai'i was the first child of Papa and Wākea, as stated in "Mele a Paku'i":

> 'O Wākeakahikoluamea
> 'O Papa, Papahānaumoku ka wahine
> Hānau Kahikikū, Kahikimoe
> Hānau Ke'āpapanu'u
> Hānau Ke'āpapalani

opposite

Palila, Pu'u La'au, island of Hawai'i
Loxioides bailleui

The palila has evolved a highly specific diet: the fantastic finch-like bill enables it to feed on the seeds of the endemic māmane (Sophora chrysophylla). *This preference for* māmane *makes the* palila *highly vulnerable to weather-related annual fluctuations in seed availability. Although no other birds have the ability to break through these hard pods and feed on the somewhat toxic seeds, the* palila *have declined.*

The subalpine dry forest habitat of the māmane *and* palila *is one of the most threatened in Hawai'i. Feral cattle and other animals feed on seedlings and enable fire-promoting grasses to invade the very limited range of the* palila*. Fire could devastate the small population, nearly all of which lives in a single location.*

Photo by Jack Jeffrey

Hānau Hawai‘i, ka moku makahiapo
Keiki makahiapo a lāua
‘O Wākea lāua ‘o Kāne
‘O Papa Walinu‘u ka wahine

It was Wākeakahikoluamea
It was Papa, Papahānaumoku, the woman
(Papa the woman who gives birth to islands)
Born was the upper horizon, the lower horizon
Born were the lower heavens
Born were the upper heavens
Born was Hawai‘i the first-born island child
The eldest, first-born child of theirs
Of Wākea together with Kāne
And Papa of Walinu‘u was the woman

Being the *hiapo*, or the eldest island child, of Wākea and Kāne, Mauna Kea (and Hawai‘i) takes on the birthrights and also the responsibilities of the firstborn. As with its counterparts in the *hiapo* philosophy of the original people, Mauna Kea takes responsibility for all under its care, and gives of its resources for the growth and well-being of the *mokupuni*.

The Importance of Kāneikawaiola, Water

The Wākea and Papa beliefs and practices have flowed from the dim past to contemporary times. The tribute and respect for *hiapo* and *kūpuna*, whether they are people or land features, has wound its way into the present. The thread of ancestral memory reminds us that the mountain, like our parents, is the wellspring and provider of physical and spiritual nourishment. A song written by Liko Martin in the 1980s reiterates the innate feeling and memory passed on to us from the time of Wākea to today for *hiapo* and *kūpuna* as providers:

ALL HAWAI‘I STANDS TOGETHER: ‘ONIPA‘A

From the fiery pit of Tūtū Pele
I hear my mother's call
Old Tūtū Kāne and Mauna Kea

Naio flower
Myoporum sandwicense

Naio *is a dry-forest/coastal shrub or tree found in association with* māmane *on the western slopes of Mauna Kea but also relatively common elsewhere throughout Hawai'i.*

The somewhat fragrant wood of naio, *or false sandalwood, served as a poor substitute after most of the true sandalwood trees had been cut for export. Naio was frequently used in the building of Hawaiian houses.*
Photo by Jack Jeffrey

Send their love to all
To stand as one beneath the sun
Blessings from Haleakalā
For our sweet Ka'ala and Wai'ale'ale
Where the greatest waters fall.

Strands of information from the past exist today and are recognized in songs and people's actions. Songs remind us of what was important during the days of our struggling ancestors. Nothing has really changed; we still need the basic resources such as land, air, water and food. Both Liko's song and Kawēkiu's name chant remind us of water. Water is a vital element of life and living. The songs remind us of the entities responsible for water. Liko credits all the mountains throughout the *pae 'āina*, or archipelago, of Hawai'i for the abundance of water we receive *ma kai*. Kawēkiu's name chant mentions Kāne and Lono as the ones who provide a lot of atmospheric water, so much water that the erosion and valley-building process is ongoing. Kāne is also credited by our ancestors as the provider of underground water. Both songs hint that mountains are synonymous with water. These high mountains attract clouds, then the clouds shed their water, and the water soaks into the earth.

Horizontal and Vertical Land Divisions

The most familiar divisions when talking about the Islands are the vertical ones. The vertical divisions are the common sections found on today's maps, and the boundary lines run from the mountain to the ocean. The vertical boundaries depended upon the mountains, rivers, streams, and cinder cones as the demarcation features. These were considered political boundaries because they separated the chiefdoms. Some of these are known as *ahupua'a*. There are still smaller vertical land sections within the *ahupua'a*.

Horizontal divisions, in contrast, did not use land features to demarcate boundaries, but used instead the vegetation growth. Vegetation growth, or the forest, was the food source and therefore a vital system for the continuum of life and life cycles. The trees housed the seeds and/or spores for regeneration. They also acted as food sources for birds, insects, animals, and man. The forest provided vegetation used

Kanahele

for medicinal and spiritual purposes, adornment, housing, dyes, clothing, games, and many other useful things.

The typical horizontal divisions that were recognized by our ancestors are still recognized today. Here are the names of some of these horizontal spaces and the kinds of flora typical of each:

Kuahiwi. The mountaintop. A very sacred area because of its height.

Kualono. The region near the mountaintop. Very little vegetation grows in this area. The *māmane* and *naio* are the only hardy trees to grow here. Both of these are hardwood trees. The flower of the *māmane* was special to the *aliʻi*; when wanting a special lei he sent his runners to fetch this flower because of its shape and yellow color. *ʻAʻaliʻi* can also be found at this height.

Wao maʻukele. The region named because of the wet, soggy ground. This area is located in the rain belt of the island, especially on the *koʻolau* side of each island. The trees of this area are the very large koa and *ʻōhiʻa*, varieties of lobelia, and *māmane*. These are the typical trees of the area. There are other trees, but the koa and the *ʻōhiʻa* dominate the canopy.

Wao akua. The forested region below the *wao maʻukele*. This is said to be occupied by spirits of the forest. Mankind seldom ventured into this area during ancestral times, except when a particular kind of tree was needed and could not be found elsewhere. The large trees acquired from the *wao akua* and the *wao maʻukele* deserved substantial offerings. This is the region where the forest had a greater variety of trees. The trees in this area should be healthy so as to supply seeds and regenerate new growth to keep the forest alive. Some of the trees and plants found are *hōʻawa, kōpiko, maile, maua, alani,* koa, and *ʻōhiʻa.*

Wao kanaka. The forested region *ma kai* of the *wao akua.* This area was frequented by man. He found wood for weapons, making his house, tools, surfboards, and canoe accessories; he also harvested dye, collected medicine and bird feathers, gathered vegetation for lei, gathered vegetation for the *kuahu,* material for making rope, and many other useful things for everyday living. The trees in the *wao akua* are also found in this area, but the trees may be smaller. Other flora found in this

area are *pilo, hāpu'u, hōlei, pāpala, hau kuahiwi, palapalai, 'ōlapa,* and *māmaki,* to name a few.

Kula.   The upland grassy plains. Some areas of an island had a very large *kula* area, as opposed to other areas that had very narrow or no grassy land section at all. A few of the most well known plants of the *kula* area are *'ilima ma'o, 'ama'u, 'a'ali'i, uluhe,* and *pili.*

Kahakai.   The edge of the ocean. At the *kahakai* were found the *niu, hala, kauna'oa, kamani, hau, milo, naupaka, lama,* and *alahe'e.* All these plants were useful to the Hawaiian and made life bearable for man on these islands.

Philosophy and Relationship to the Forest

These divisions provide the following insights into what was and is important to the quality of life for the Hawaiian—his relationship to his environment, and especially his relationship to the land—because he was and is a creature of the land.

🌿 Hawaiians recognized and acknowledged the importance of vegetation. Land sections are identified by the change of flora—thick vegetation in the lower forests to thin vegetation in the uplands, and grassy upland plains to lowland/beach vegetation.

🌿 Hawaiians put high cultural value on older or larger trees and thick *kīpuka* that normally housed older trees.

🌿 Hawaiians did not as a matter of course penetrate the *wao ma'ukele* or *wao akua* if the trees they needed could be gotten elsewhere, because of the priority of promoting new growth through non-disturbance of seed-producing forest areas.

🌿 Hawaiians realized the importance of the food source and the regenerative energy of the forest. Therefore it was necessary to leave some areas or groves of trees as they stood originally, thus the name *wao akua.*

Kanahele

'ŌANAPELE ✌

Kapulani Landgraf

Hakakaupili ka pueo makalulu i ka pali o Huelo,
ho'okūlanalana nā lau kea o Pele.
Konāhau i ka māulukua o 'O'opuloa,
kokolo hele ka uhiwai ma luna o ke ala o Pi'ilani.
Ho'ope'e 'o Ka'ahuali'i ma kahi o ke ala pali o Ke'ohekanu,
puhipau ka makani 'ākiukiu i ke kani o ka hinihini konouli.

Owl with still eyes stands intently watching over the cliffs of Huelo;
the gray stones of Pele are unsettled.
Cold penetrates the upland forest of 'O'opuloa;
thick mist creeps over the path of Pi'ilani.
Ka'ahuali'i hides along hillside paths of Ke'ohekanu;
'ākiukiu winds reveal the cry of the land snail.

opposite
'Ōanapele, Maui
Photo by Kapulani Landgraf

PUʻU KUKUI 🌿

Kapulani Landgraf

ʻO Kukui ka piko o ka mauna o Kahalawai,
kū kiʻekiʻe ʻo ʻAheleakalā ma luna o ke kihi poʻohiwi i ke kuaola.
I Kukui nō ka waiho ʻana a ka wai kapu a Kāne,
i pili aloha ʻo ʻEke i ka ua ʻAwa.
Kupu kelakela ke poʻo i ʻālohilohi me ka lehua makanoe,
apo ʻia ʻo Kukui e nā kualono o Kahoʻolewa.

Kukui is the piko of the Kahalawai mountains,
ʻAheleakalā rising regally above its verdant living shoulders.
Kukui is the repository of the sacred waters of Kāne,
ʻEke, a steadfast companion in the ʻAwa mist.
The summit reveals the brilliance of the lehua makanoe,
Kukui embraced by the surrounding ridges of Kahoʻolewa.

MAKAMAKA'OLE 🐚
Kapulani Landgraf

Noho 'o Hina i uka o Makaliua,
pūhuli nā puanui i ka ulu lā'au a Kanaloa.
Palemo ka uhu pākali o Hulu,
hūnākele 'o Māui i ka lapa o Makamaka'ole.
Piliāmo'o ka wai ea i ka palipa'a o 'Eke,
pōlani ka wai 'apo i Laha'ole.

Hina dwells in the uplands of Makaliua,
abundant blossoms thickly growing in Kanaloa's forest.
Uhu of Hulu allures then vanishes
Māui concealed on Makamaka'ole ridge.
Life's fluids clinging to 'Eke's rocky cliffs,
pure water captured at Laha'ole.

opposite

Makamaka'ole, Maui

*The West Maui mountains are
a highly productive watershed.
Water slowly seeps from bogs like
'Eke Crater (at top) and filters
down the mountain, eventually
recharging aquifers and streams.*

*West Maui landowners have
realized the life-sustaining
importance of this process and
have protected the upland forests
through the West Maui Watershed Partnership and the Natural
Area Partnership of Pu'u Kukui.*

*These public–private partner-
ships ensure the best hope for
the future of the forests and
the fresh water that is their
most valuable product.*

Photo by Kapulani Landgraf

INVENTORY OF A KOA 🌿

Rob Pacheco

It is a big tree. It rises above the canopy of the *kīpuka* with sculptured grace. Its trunk is as thick as a bus. The branches are larger than most other trees' trunks. It is a koa. I visit the tree often, with hundreds of visits over the years. Only after a dozen visits did I see how expansively its crown truly spread. Nearly every visit brings a new discovery of this great creature. It is ancient and noble. And it is generous. The life that exists on, around, and in this monarch of the forest is remarkable. The tree is more than just itself, it is the sum of all that make it their home. This koa contains a priceless inventory of life.

Nearly 25 feet in circumference, over 100 feet tall, and with a crown-spread of close to 150 feet, the koa has plenty of room for all sorts of organisms. The first things I noticed were all the epiphytes. Epiphytes are plants that grow on other plants. In rainforests, just about any plant can grow epiphytically, including other trees. There is a 20-foot tall *'ōhi'a lehua* growing in the crotch of the main fork in the trunk of the koa. It's a pretty little *'ōhi'a* that has a fine perch above the fern floor below. Three other species of trees and shrubs grow on the koa. At its base, a half dozen *'ōlapa* trees, with their antiseptic, turpentine odor, grow on the thick koa roots that crawl along the forest floor. There is also a *pūkiawe* and an *'ōhelo*, which have taken hold next to each other on a large root. Unlike the small shrubs one finds on the lava flows, these individuals are small trees, ten to fifteen feet tall.

Ferns, mosses, lichens, molds, and fungi account for the great majority of plants on the koa. About 60 feet up, along a major branch, the shuttlecock fern, *Dryopteris wallichiana* rises up in its distinctive shape of a badminton birdie. Besides the *Dryopteris*, there are lots of other ferns sprouting on the koa. *'Ekaha*, or Hart's tongue (*Elaphoglossum* spp.), ferns are perhaps the most numerous, with long, tongue-like fronds. Two tiny little finger ferns grow in bunches right next to one another, the *kolokolo* (*Grammitis tenella*) and the small, serrated *kihe* (*Lellingeria saffordii*). Three different *Asplenium* ferns find moist little crannies to their satisfaction. Many parts of the tree are covered in various mosses. Some are thick and spongy, others

are thin and slimy. Most of the upper, smaller branches are draped in the yellow, stringy lichen that looks like Spanish moss. There is a bright green mold in one spot of damp shade that appears to be the same stuff that grows so easily on bread in Hawai'i. Below the mold is a large table-bract fungus. Yellow-white, it is smooth and cool to touch and leaves a lovely aromatic mushroom scent on the fingers.

My favorite epiphyte is the *'ala'ala wai nui* (peperomia herb). Its beauty is hidden from casual view; from the top it looks like a plain green plant with small pointed leaves. Turn the leaves over and an exquisite deep variegated maroon color is revealed. From the ground looking up into the tree, the *'ala'ala wai nui* glows with color as the sunlight passes through from above. They are precious, twinkling tree ornaments.

Koa Bug
Pu'u Koa
Coleotichus blackburniae

The koa bug is the largest endemic true bug. It is found on all islands associated with its host species, koa, as well as a'ali'i, which is host to a luminous yellow variety. The decline of this insect is directly related to the introduction of insects for biocontrol of agricultural pests.
Photo by Jack Jeffrey

The invertebrate residents of the koa are numerous. There is a large honeybee hive in a cavity from a broken branch. It is a significant nest, with honeycomb visible from the ground and black propolis stains leaking down the trunk. *Plagithmysus varians* is a cute little triangular woodborer whose larvae provide an important food source for forest songbirds. The koa bug *(Coleotichus blackburniae)* is the largest native bug. Its back is dimpled with dots of iridescent green and blue. Spiders are usually easily found in the bark and in small cavities. The long-jawed, humpbacked, spiny-legged spider (no description needed after the common name!) has the wonderful scientific moniker *Tetragnathas quasimodo*. Although in the orb-weaver family, it has given up building a web and hunts its prey raptorially. Once, at night, I discovered the largest spider I've ever seen in the native forest. It was a comb's footed spider that was bright rusty orange, just like the orange rust, mold, or lichen growing on the tree's bark. Three to three-and-a-half inches long, its arched abdomen gave off a metallic sheen. I have yet to find one again.

Partly because of the tree's invertebrate wealth, it is a fabulous place for birds. The great koa has given me hours of enjoyable bird watching. I have observed every bird species found in the forest along its trunks and limbs or foraging among its leaves and flowers. ʻIo, the Hawaiian hawk, has perched in its branches. Family groups of endangered Hawaiʻi creepers and the ʻakiapōlāʻau have gleaned insects from its wood and bark. ʻAmakihi, ʻapapane, and ʻiʻiwi frequent the tree for insects and nectar. ʻŌmaʻo has nested for two seasons within a small hole in a limb. ʻElepaio flit around catching bugs, flies, and moths. Turkeys roost for the night, as do kalij pheasants. A Japanese white-eye once took a bath in a fresh pool of rainwater caught in a crack of the tree. There are always birds to be found within the koa.

The koa is a treasure chest in the forest. Its existence provides for a richness of life that is uniquely Hawaiian. Yes, there is value in a koa picture frame, a hand-turned bowl, or a handcrafted furniture piece. But how can you value the richness of a living tree?

'Elepaio
Chasiempis sandwichensis

*If you are in the forest and see a small
brown bird curiously perching near
your head, it is most likely an 'elepaio.
They are one of the most sociable of
native birds and renowned for their
mischief and ability to guide people to
the best canoe logs. The 'elepaio is also
perhaps the world's most versatile bird
in terms of foraging habitat.*
Photo by Jack Jeffrey

'Anianiao
Hemignathus parvus

This smallest of the remaining native Hawaiian birds is endemic to the island of Kaua'i. There it is relatively widespread in the upland forests, where it is able to tolerate significant habitat disturbance from alien plants.
Photo by Jack Jeffrey

'ŌHI'A ❧ ADVENTURES WITH A GENETIC MARVEL

P. Quentin Tomich

opposite

'Ōhi'a Lehua, Hualālai, island of Hawai'i
Metrosideros polymorpha

As the Latin name polymorpha *suggests,* 'ōhi'a *is found in many forms and in many diverse ecosystems, from recent lava flows to high mountain bogs. It is one of the most prominent trees in wet and mesic native forests and can range from sea level to high elevations. The* 'ōhi'a's *wide distribution and variety of forms make it an integral part of many ecosystems, biologically and culturally. Considered sacred by Hawaiians, it was carved by specially trained carpenters for use in temples. The* lehua *(blossoms) are associated with the goddess Pele.*
Photo by Franco Salmoiraghi

Botanists suggest that the *'ōhi'a* was established in Hawai'i through a single colonization. It could mean that just one of its tiny, aerodynamic seeds surviving in our remote islands could have started the amazing complex that formed a dominant forest cover over nearly all of Hawai'i. Well, let's say it was a chance shower of seeds that wafted thousands of miles from somewhere in the Indo-Pacific region. That in itself would be a remarkable event. *'Ōhi'a* retains this ability to cruise on the wind and to thrive wherever conditions are favorable. It is the first tree to colonize fresh lava flows. When older forests fail through the natural mechanism of "dieback," new seed rains from the local sky bearing fresh genetic material that selectively renews the forest. It is an ongoing process. You can see it along the Saddle Road above Hilo.

'Ōhi'a is named botanically *Metrosideros* (literally "ironwood," in reference to its hard wood). The principal species is *M. polymorpha*, which, indeed, is descriptive of its "many forms." This species is further recognized as having eight botanical "varieties." In addition, there are four other *Metrosideros* species in Hawai'i, generally occurring as shrubs or small trees, that are an added delight to the more avid systematic botanists.

The *'ōhi'a* group contains versatile trees that successfully occupy many ecological niches. Examples: The *'ōhi'a* of the acidic boglands above Waimea, on the island of Hawai'i, grows to the height of only a foot or so. That it matures and regularly produces blossoms in that static condition of growth is indeed remarkable. And the hardy, sparse population seen at 7,000- to 8,000-feet elevations along the Mauna Loa Trail is resistant to nightly frosts there, whereas its close relatives at 3,500 feet, only a few miles below, are badly damaged in "frost pockets" charged infrequently with icy winter air.

The Polynesian settlers of Hawai'i and their descendants, over a thousand years or more ago, gradually cleared large areas of the lower lands of the Hāmākua Coast to about the 2,000-foot level. Later, planting of sugarcane finally wiped out the forest except for remnants in the gulches and on sea cliffs, some of which remain today. Upland forests were decimated by feral cattle and ranching, with rather few small tracts unused for agriculture set aside in a system of forest reserves. It was a gradual process. Speaking about the lands between Honoka'a and Waimea in 1856, Curtis Lyons wrote, "where now hardly a tree is to be seen for miles, we were informed by an old resident, that 25 years ago he lost himself with his team in the woods." Cattle were cited as the cause of this depletion.

With the opening of Āhualoa Homesteads in 1895, there was a new wave of forest clearing by the homesteaders to prepare the land for crops and pasture. A demand for wood, especially 'ōhi'a, to fire the sugar factory boilers and to supply the needs of the residential camps was an added incentive for tree cutting. William F. Mendes (1907–1999) related that his father had contracts for wood delivery. Some family members cut the trees into logs, and others, Bill included, transported the products to the plantation with ox teams and wagons. The elder Mendes had several teams of three yoke each (six animals) for the work. It was heavy going, mostly downhill over rough trails. Coming down from Āhualoa, after crossing Ni'eni'e Gulch, the route departed from the main Homestead Road and came down approximately on the track of what is now Plumeria Street. In Honoka'a, the logs were dropped at the head of the plantation cable railway, just above the Hāmākua Ditch, for transport to the mill yard.

In 1959, this site was the County Base Yard. The Dan Johnasen residence (since dismantled) was right there in the middle of Haina Hill Road, and all traffic to and from the mill passed abruptly around it. Walter Teves (b. 1919) has noted that as a boy he and some friends used to meet the ox teams coming down from Āhualoa and help with braking on steeper grades by tugging on the rope attached to the brake lever. This in turn pressed the brake shoes to the rear wagon wheels. The drover did not ride the loaded wagon, but walked alongside the team and usually handled the braking himself. Walter states that the oxen were well trained and came to feed every morning for yoking. Each animal knew its place in the team. One of the Mendes ox yokes is still in the extended family and was shown at a Western Week Museum in Honoka'a about 1976.

Abraham Caires (1892–1983), also a son of an original Āhualoa Homestead family, told of clearing the lands. One incident relates to the large size of some of the standing 'ōhi'a. One tree was said to have taken two and a half days to cut down

'Akohekohe
Palmeria dolei

Alighting on the crimson lehua *flowers, the* 'akohekohe *of Maui is easily distinguished by its sizable tuft of feathers above the beak. The* 'akohekohe *spends most of its time feeding on* lehua *nectar and is likely one of the tree's most active pollinators.*
Photo by Jack Jeffrey

Kamehameha butterfly
Lepelepeohina; Pulehua Kamehameha
Vanessa tameamea

The Kamehameha butterfly, seen here on a lehua *blossom, is more often associated with its host plant,* māmaki (Pipturus *spp.). This insect is another victim of parasitizing wasps introduced for biocontrol of alien crop pests.*
Photo by Jack Jeffrey

ʻŌhiʻa forest, Kaʻūpūlehu,
island of Hawaiʻi.
Photo by Franco Salmoiraghi

with a two-man crosscut saw. This certainly rivals our largest trees of Kalōpā State Park. We have trunk diameters (at four and a half feet above ground) of forty-two to fifty-two inches. The very largest, on the Nature Trail, near Station 25, measures sixty-six inches in diameter.

Such large trees were scattered about in Hāmākua, and some are still standing. It is probable that the relatively undisturbed tract of Kalōpā State Park, at 2,000–2,300 feet is a good representative of the original ʻōhiʻa forest in our district. Very little is left elsewhere. Some ʻōhiʻa have survived on steep slopes of the larger gulches. We found one giant tree in Kalōpā Gulch, at 1,400 feet, at the back of our farm (on a state-owned portion of the gulch slope). Unfortunately, it was toppled and well weathered when first noted in 1990, but it remains as an impressive hulk of a tree, some thirty-two inches in stem diameter.

The age of trees in the subtropics, where severe winters are unknown, and annual growth rings are not rigidly fixed, cannot be determined by examining these increments. A seasoned botanist visiting Kalōpā Park was asked to estimate the ages of our old trees. He replied that many factors, including age, apply to size. "But, your largest trees might just be in the bracket of 300 to 500 years." This seems reasonable. Perhaps these scattered giants are survivors from another time, and the forest in general is a new cohort of trees. We need some detailed studies.

There is some information from our records. When the building site was cleared of all but the largest trees in 1969, some natural regeneration followed on bare sunny ground. Along the roadside near the Park Information Center are three clusters of several trees, survivors from this event. It will be useful to know how large these trees will be at 100 years of age. That is only about seventy years from now. Young folks of today should check them out in the year 2069.

LOULU 🪸 OUR NATIVE FAN PALMS

P. Quentin Tomich

Loulu colonized Hawai'i in very ancient times via fruits borne on sea currents. There may have been only one instance of arrival and establishment, or just a few. The source was perhaps Fiji, Samoa, or Tonga, where fan palms similar to ours still persist. In the rich and diverse habitats of Hawai'i, founder stocks have evolved over the eons into about nineteen endemic species. These are distributed on all major islands, and one survives, even today, on the isolated remnant rock mass of Nihoa (153 acres) as it, geologically speaking, crumbles into oblivion. Nihoa arose from the sea some 7.5 million years ago and was once a large shield volcano.

An even more remarkable site is Huelo Island, a sea stack, just off the windward coast of Moloka'i. This islet is a remnant lava column 125 feet high. Its sloping surface cap of probably much less than an acre is almost totally covered by a crown to crown mass of *loulu* about twenty feet tall. If you are bent on examining *loulu* groves, this is a must-see example.

The *loulu* and other fan palms have characteristic leaves (fronds) with a long flattened stem (petiole) and a large, fan-shaped blade strengthened by longitudinal creases between blade elements. One diagnostic feature of our Hawaiian *loulu*, and its immediate ancestors (genus *Pritchardia*) of the South Pacific, is that the petiole is unarmed. Other fan palms of the world, with few exceptions, are equipped at each edge of the stem with a row of sharp, thorny, and often hooked, spines. Spines may occur only near the base of the stem, but if it has any spiny armament at all it is not a *Pritchardia*.

The Big Island has about five of the nineteen described Hawaiian species of *loulu*, and two or three of these occur in Hāmākua (there is much to be learned about the characteristics and distribution of the forms). I was intrigued years ago by an early botanical report that described a remnant population of tall *loulu* on the slopes of Mauna Kea, "between Mana and Honoka'a." The authors named their find *Pritchardia montis-kea*. In 1909 there were three surviving trees, and on a later visit, in 1921, only one remained. This small population, probably isolated on open

opposite

Loulu
Pritchardia schattaueri

This loulu, *endemic to the island of Hawai'i, is one of twenty-three endemic* loulu *species in Hawai'i, most of which are in danger of extinction in their natural habitat.*
Photo by David Liittschwager and Susan Middleton

Huelo islet off Moloka'i

Isolation on this small islet off Moloka'i has allowed this population of Pritchardia hillebrandii *to thrive. Elsewhere in Hawai'i* Pritchardia *species have not fared so well, and* loulu *are some of the rarest plants in the world.*
Photo by Frans Lanting

range, was said to be crowded toward extinction by the ravages of rats and pigs that ate the fruits and seedlings.

A second Hāmākua *loulu*, *Pritchardia lanigera*, is well established on Kohala Mountain, in the rain forest and boglands of the plateau west of Waimanu Valley. On one of several hiking-camping trips into this region by youthful adventurers from the Honokaʻa area, a photo of *P. lanigera* was taken near the "new USGS Camp" cabin. Long neglected and vacant, the shelter there has since collapsed.

When I had read of *P. montis-kea* and its rarity back in the 1920s, I wondered if perhaps it had ever been taken into cultivation. Had some cattleman, cowboy, or sugar planter secured seed and planted it somewhere along the coast at a ranch house, at a labor camp, or at a sugar company management residence? An interesting idea. It would be important to continue the search for cultivated *loulu* in our communities to compare with originally collected *P. montis-kea* and *P. lanigera*. I am awaiting the day when someone contacts me with a story such as, "You should see our *loulu* palms. My great grandfather brought the seed home from the ranch back in 1924."

At Kalōpā State Park, we introduced two species of *loulu* for the arboretum. *P. beccariana*, which came from the vicinity of Glenwood, and *P. affinis*, which is from lowland stock of Kaʻū. The first of these is a rainforest plant and the second is typically coastal, a useful food and fiber plant apparently spread widely to Puna shoreline villages and around through Kona to South Kohala.

In the park, *P. beccariana* was slow to take hold, but after about twenty years several of a dozen or so planted have reached heights of fifteen to twenty-five feet. The *P. affinis* may miss the coastal sunshine but are surviving at five to ten feet tall. As such, both species are good representatives of *loulu* for local study.

LAND AND LITERATURE 🌿
TEACHING ABOUT THE HAWAIIAN FOREST
Jan Becket

opposite
Koʻiahi Valley, Mākua, Oʻahu

This beautiful valley, part of the Mākua Military Reservation on Oʻahu, is rich in native resources. It is known for its remnant lama (Diospyros sandwicensis) *forest and* maile lau liʻi, *small-leaved maile (Alyxia oliviformis). Maile is one of the five standard plants used in an altar to Laka, the goddess of hula. Mākua Valley and its natural and cultural resources are considered sacred by many Hawaiians. Fire and introduced grasses continue to threaten these resources.*

Photo by Jan Becket

Loina, or traditional practice, helps you connect with the land . . . as the ancient natives did. The winds, the trees, everything becomes living, personified. SAM GON III

In his celebrated environmental manifesto, *The Rediscovery of North America* (New York: Vintage Books, 1990), environmentalist and author Barry Lopez agrees with Sam Gon when Lopez proposes a new ethic for human tenure on the land: "It is by looking upon the land not as its possessor but as a companion. To achieve this, one must I think cultivate intimacy, as one would with a human being."

I teach a high school senior elective called Land and Literature. We begin the semester reading Lopez, who describes the 1492 European "incursion" into North America as a series of greedy raids that set the tone for what followed, a "profound abuse of the place," that continues today. Ultimately, though, his is a message of hope; the ethic that he advances redefines our relationship with the land as communion with a place that we accept, finally, as home, with all of the obligations that implies: "The true wealth that America offered, wealth that could turn exploitation into residency, greed into harmony, was to come from one thing—the cultivation and achievement of local knowledge."

The course Land and Literature asks students to further that acquisition of "local knowledge," of the places they live in and care about. We begin first, during the forty-minute period, with direct observation and description of places not far from the classroom. Despite distractions, most students connect:

I walk up a steep hill on stairs made of rocks, and I am continuing to be bitten by the abundance of pesky bugs and scraped by the sharp thorns of those ridiculous thorn trees. Mosquitoes constantly swarm around and suck out my life, little by little, as I try to complete this assignment. It is a very arduous task to carry out as I am constantly being distracted by these annoying things. But through the thickest of the bugs and trees I see a large rock in the middle of all these things; I stare at it in awe.
TUPU LAUFOU, 3/14/03

opposite

*Examples from land journals of
students Adam Mendez-Ancheta (left)
and Gilbert Visser (right), Land and
Literature class, Kamehameha
Schools, 2003.*

Wherever they go to describe their surroundings, students are encouraged to focus on the details, the small stuff. Just going to a place and describing what is there proves surprisingly demanding because it requires one's full attention:

I noticed a couple of dried-up cactus plants turning a brownish ugly color and I mistook it for a tree trunk; that's how deformed it was. I also noticed on the ledge above the cave, in the rocks, two baby cacti and a couple of tall grasses or, really, weeds.
KAʻONOHI SEGOVIA, MARCH 2003

The places we go sometimes have cultural significance. Those who know volunteer to make an entrance chant, *Kūnihi Ka Mauna*, and then the class respectfully enters, looks around carefully, and then goes a little distance away to describe and sketch. Again, the small details bring the place to life again on the page:

I saw three different levels of platforms up on the hill. On the top left corner there is a formation of medium sized stones. Below it there is a stone standing upright known as the Kū stone and below that is a flatter big stone known as Hina, the male and female stones. To the right of those are the other two platforms. The higher one consists of smaller stones while the lower one is made up of larger stones for the foundation. This separation shows it was carefully planned and built. JASON LAEHA, 2/7/03

We continue to visit nearby places throughout the semester, especially on hot days with just the right amount of breeze to push away mosquitoes. Students by then have favorite places and ask to go to those for the period. In addition, though, they keep a land journal, a kind of record of their interaction with a place they have chosen. Lopez calls this a "*querencia,*" a place from which one draws strength. In local terms, though, it is their *ahupuaʻa,* and their strength is *mana.* Some choose the uplands, the *wao nahele* and *kuahiwi:*

A calm breeze blows through the trees making the branches rustle like the crashing of waves on the sand. The air is light on the tongue. . . . The ground is covered with pine needles dried from years of untouched growth. The silence is peaceful. Moss covers the ground, creating a carpet-like texture, roots travel in and out of the ground, intertwining with earth, creating a sense of untouched beauty. Much of the pathway consists of narrow walkways atop towering steep cliffs. The summit is a large open area

Becket

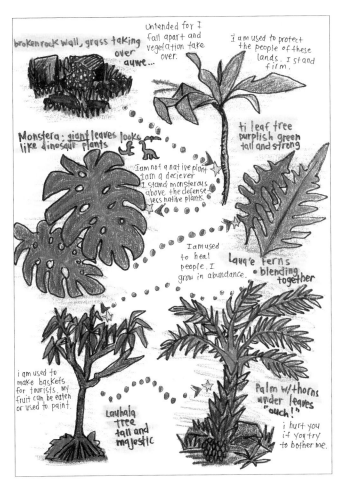

broken rock wall, grass taking over auwe...

untended for I fall apart and vegetation take over.

I am used to protect the people of these lands. I stand firm.

Monstera: giant leaves looks like dinosaur plants

ti leaf tree purplish green tall and strong

I am not a native plant I am a deciever I stand monsterous above the defense-less native plants.

I am used to heal people. I grow in abundance.

Laua'e ferns blending together

i am used to make baskets for tourists. MY fruit can be eaten or used to paint.

Lauhala tree tall and majestic

Palm w/thorns under leaves "ouch!"

i hurt you if you try to bother me.

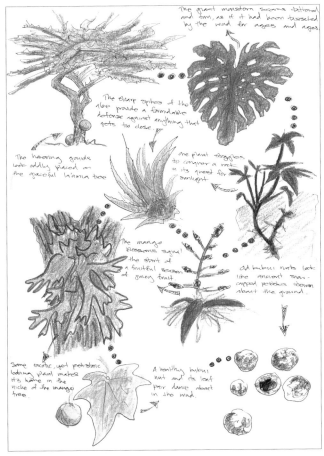

The giant monstera seems tattered and torn, as if it had been tousseled by the wind for ages and ages.

The sharp spikes of the 'löe provide a formidable defense against anything that gets too close.

The haaening gjands look oddly placed on the graceful la'amia tree

one plant struggles to conquer a rock in its quest for sunlight.

The mango blossoms signal the start of a fruitful season of juicy fruit.

old kukui nuts look like ancient snow-capped pebbles strewn about the ground.

Some exotic, yet prehistoric looking plant makes its home in the niche of the mango tree.

A healthy kukui nut and its leaf pair dance about in the wind.

*encircled by trees. The opening gives a sense of jubilance; one will often dwell in the
moment before wanting to leave the euphoric experience.*
ADAM MENDEZ-ANCHETA, FEBRUARY 2003

Some choose *ke kai*, the seashore:

*The setting sun casts a flattering shadow against Puʻu o Hulu Kai, magnifying itself
over Māʻili Point. Pink, purple, and orange colors spray themselves across the evening
sky: a sunset. It's evident that Ulehawa is calming down. That gracious sun, which
provides life for all, loses strength and settles into the ocean.*

 *The ocean moves slower than before with fewer waves crashing against the shore-
line. All life knows evening is upon us. The shy moon illuminates itself against the
dark Nānākuli sky, causing the rocks to cast minuscule shadows against the sand
along Ulehawa's shoreline. Fewer people comb the beach; some look for an area to
call their own, others gather fish to feed their families. The sand crabs race along the
water, ducking into their holes at the approach of anyone. Luckily a slight wind gath-
ers strength, bringing the sand up in a whirlwind, carrying itself out into the sea, with
all the little crabs fleeing as well.* JAMIE KUTARA, FEBRUARY 2003

We also do an exercise called "modeling," in which students put their own words
and meanings into a form created by someone else, just another way to bring them
into contact with others who have the same feelings for the landscape. Some of their
models are sensitive reactions to a place, with awareness in time as well as space.

KOʻOLAU
Haunani-Kay Trask

light in the crevice
never seen mosses
palai kālā ʻau
bamboo

crescent moon
stones
fragrant clack clack
from the shadows

KAPĀLAMA
Shelly Smith

night in the room
never been noises
pigs cats
whispers

full moon
shadows
trees sway lightly
from the breeze

hunehune rain	cold rain
aloft on the wind	drips on the roof
steamy rocks	ancient stones
falls of crustaceans	days of old
blue caves far	small platforms far
away choked	away crowded
with grasses wet	with grasses weeds
fully winged	fully grown
high ʻiwa floating	small kōlea pecking
many chambered	for worms
heavens still	Alaska bound
and singing	and flying

Clearly, some students come to the course with "local knowledge" of their own *ahupuaʻa*. For those, the course merely confirms something they already possess. Similarly, the literature we read together confirms something already embedded in the *kaʻao* and *moʻolelo* of this place, Hawaiʻi. We read the portion of the journey of Hiʻiakaikapoliopele and Wahineʻōmaʻo around the windward coast of Oʻahu, on the way to pick up Lohiʻau, on Kauaʻi. The story of their journey is not merely a tale of passion, intrigue, and conquest, but a relating of the acquisition of *mana* through intimacy with places in the landscape. The lover adored by Hiʻiaka on her travels through Kailua, Kanahau, is not just a handsome *aliʻi* but an upright stone at the *heiau* bearing his name. A large stone still at that *heiau* appears to be the same one identified in the 1930s as Kanahau. Pōhaku o Kauaʻi is not just a stone at Kaʻena Point, but the grandfather of Pele, a stone to be addressed with the respect due a *kupuna*.

If "Hiʻiakaikapoliopele" is like a "chick flick," with the two women throughout their journey attracting and sometimes destroying men who cannot help but fall under their erotic power, then *Kamapuaʻa* is the opposite, a tale for guys. As a counterpoint to the former, we read, sometimes out loud, the story of the battle between Kamapuaʻa and Pele, just a small portion of the epic. The fire goddess almost defeats him, burning his bristles, but the clever little pig narrowly escapes by assuming his fish form, the *humuhumunukunukuāpuaʻa*. Renewed, he returns, seduces a willing

Pele and quickly triumphs by pinning her down in an embarrassing position for days on end, repeatedly violating her. Like all Hawaiian tales, the story contains multiple levels of meaning, one of which is the observation of the contest between vegetation and lava; first one wins, and then the other. Neither will completely triumph. Thus, Hawaiian literature is not just "literature" in the Western sense, but a way of knowing this place, based on centuries of direct observation, based on the "local knowledge" mentioned by Lopez. As Kamapua'a repeatedly asserts, "I am of this place."

Ultimately, both tales affirm kinship with the land, what Lopez refers to as "indigenous systems of natural philosophy." Wayne Westlake repeats the same idea in the poem "Hawaiians Eat Fish": "Hawaiians / eat / fish / eat / Hawaiians/ eat / fish / eat / Hawaiians / eat / fish / eat / Hawaiians." However, if this system of ancient knowledge is now submerged beneath freeways and condominiums here, as elsewhere, Lopez decries its fragmentation:

We lost in this manner whole communities of people, plants, and animals, because a handful of men wanted gold and silver, title to land, the privileges of aristocracy, slaves, stables of little boys. We lost languages, epistemologies, books, ceremonies, systems of logic and metaphysics—a long, hideous carnage.

Lopez asks the reader to look to those whose lives model hope for an alternative future: Bartolomé de las Casas, Oscar Romero, Thomas Merton, the Amish and Mennonite communities. In a similar vein, speakers come to address the class. In their own ways they model alternative ways of knowing Hawai'i; they have helped to redefine mere real estate as land and place and kinship: Haunani-Kay Trask, who writes poems about culture and place; Chuck Burrows, who works to restore Kawai Nui Marsh; Lance LaPierre, who combines Hawaiian and Western ways of knowing in his work for the Nature Conservancy; Mahealani Cypher, whose lifelong fight against the H-3 Freeway has made her intimate with the land all along its corridor; William Aila, who works for the return of Mākua Valley; and Kapua Sproat, Kyle Kajihiro, Henry Curtis, and Kat Brady, whose work helps protect land from "the hideous carnage." There are many more.

Thus, the course looks at what is and then at what was, perhaps with a suggestion of what might have been. In response to a looming global environmental crisis that has profound local implications, it looks at environmental issues through traditional Hawaiian values embedded in traditional orature. At the end, it returns to the present, with students encouraged to write a paper on a contemporary land issue. One such paper looks closely at the windward Waiāhole water controversy:

Eventually, contact with Westerners and their ideas of economics and politics brought a new era to the Hawaiian islands, an era that led to the loss of the Hawaiian identity, culture and land. Many are still trying to recover these today. Westerners began taking over much of the land in the islands for profit. Sugar plantations became the next big investment for foreigners after the California Gold Rush. Twelve prosperous sugar plantations were actively running in the islands by 1860 (Ke Kiaʻi: A Publication of the Native Hawaiian Advisory Council, Vol. 7, No. 4, winter 1996). The price of sugar began to increase and plantations started looking for more water to grow their crops, especially since it takes 800 pounds of water to produce one pound of sugar.

The digging of the ditch was done by the newly formed Waiāhole Water Company, Ltd., now known as the Waiāhole Irrigation Company. The company did not complete the drilling of these developmental tunnels until 1963 ("Chronology of Waiāhole Ditch," Environment Hawaiʻi). The combined pumps and ditches of this system pumped 27 million gallons of water per day (mgd) to Leeward Oʻahu.

This [the Waiāhole Ditch] resulted in a big loss for much of the Kāneʻohe Bay area. This bay used to be one of the state's most fruitful estuaries, but it has lost up to 70 million gallons per day due to the ditch and other uses. Thus, much of the Bay's aquatic life has declined (Commission on Water Resource Management, "Waiāhole Ditch Information Packet") The ahupuaʻa of Waiāhole and Waikāne, the poi bowls of Oʻahu, were hit hard with the depletion of water supplies. Many kalo farmers were unable to continue growing their crops and were forced to change their ways of life, and to walk away from cultural traditions (Moses Haia, "Hawaiian Water: Waiāhole Ditch Controversy," Ke Kiaʻi: Native Hawaiian Advisory Council, Vol. 7, No. 1, spring 1996). SARA NAGATANI, FALL 2002

As Sam Gon points out, the most intimate connection of all is between the land and the language. "That all these animals and plants could be described in Hawaiian overwhelmed me—there was obviously a long-term connection between the land and the language, which I began learning." Here, once again, the students teach me far more than I could possibly offer them.

RAIN AT NIGHT ✌

W. S. Merwin

This is what I have heard

at last the wind in December
lashing the old trees with rain
unseen rain racing along the tiles
under the moon
wind rising and falling
wind with many clouds
trees in the night wind

after an age of leaves and feathers
someone dead
thought of this mountain as money
and cut the trees
that were here in the wind
in the rain at night
it is hard to say it
but they cut the sacred 'ohias then
the sacred koas then
the sandalwood and the halas
holding aloft their green fires
and somebody dead turned cattle loose
among the stumps until killing time

but the trees have risen one more time
and the night wind makes them sound
like the sea that is yet unknown
the black clouds race over the moon
the rain is falling on the last place

opposite

Koa forest with young koa trees.
Photo by Shuzo Uemoto

ALIVE IN STORY ✸
Dennis Kawaharada

In a scene from *Lāʻieikawai*, published in 1854 by S. N. Haleole, the royal child Lāʻieikawai "appears resting on the wings of birds . . . two ʻiʻiwipōlena were perched on her shoulders, shaking dew scented with *lehua* blossoms onto her head." Her foster mother Waka has the *mana* to command the forest birds to provide comfort and nourishment to her *hānai*. The scene makes a lasting impression on the reader because of precise imagery and magical realism. Waka has sequestered Lāʻieikawai in Paliuli, in the forest between Puna and Hilo, until a suitable husband can be found for her. Before her defilement by a handsome intruder, Lāʻieikawai, along with her guardians, lives idyllically: ". . . never did they weary of life. Never did they even see the person who prepared their food. The only time they saw food was when they were ready to eat; the birds brought the food to them and cleared away the remnants after they had eaten. So Paliuli became a land beloved by them, and there they dwelled happily. . . . "

Lāʻieikawai provides the reader with a pathway into the Hawaiian forest. The narrative evokes the scents, sounds, and scenery of the forest, details the flora and fauna, and fills the reader with curiosity and wonder. This is not the dark, dangerous forest of European folktales, but a sacred place, secluded but life-giving, where, with the help of spirits, the respectful visitors and dwellers find what they need. The flora and fauna are an integral part of daily life, providing materials for musical instruments (a nose flute, a kī-leaf trumpet) and adornments (a wreath made from *lehua*, a house of feathers).

We learn about the features of forest plants through the symbolic naming of characters. A group of five sisters who become protectors of Lāʻieikawai have plant names. Kahalaomāpuana—"the fragrant *hala*"—is the youngest sister. The long, thick-growing leaves of the *hala* provide shelter from both rain and sun, suggesting her protective nature. The prop roots of the *hala* suggest her firm solidity; the strong, fibrous leaves (used to weave mats) and the thorns along the edges and spine of the leaves symbolize her toughness and her warrior nature. Kahalaomāpuana becomes Lāʻieikawai's *ʻalihikaua nui* (great war chief). The core of the *hala* tree nut is called

opposite

Iʻiwi (iʻiwipōlena, Vestiaria coccinea) *on flowering* ʻōhiʻa.
Photo by Jack Jeffrey

53

pīkoi, or *'īkoi*, also a name for a weapon—a tripping club. In another story ("Kahalaopuna"), the hard *hala* nut itself becomes a weapon as a jealous lover batters his betrothed to death with one. Like the thorny rose bush in European Medieval romance, this *hala* fiercely defends the flower of her *ali'i's* virginity against unsuitable male visitors.

Kahalaomāpuana's four older sisters are named after four types of *maile: Maile-ha'iwale*, brittle-*maile*, a *maile* with small, rounded leaves; *Mailekaluhea*, fragrant *maile; Mailelauli'i*, small-leafed *maile*, a *maile* with narrow, pointed leaves; and *Mailepākaha*, common *maile* vine, a *maile* with blunt ovate leaves.

Because of their fragrance, the four sisters are sent by their brother 'Aiwohikupua to entice Lā'ieikawai out of hiding, so he can court her. But the *maile* sisters are weaker than Kahalaomāpuana and dependent on her strength, as is the *maile* vine itself, which is found straggling on the ground or twining around nearby shrubs and trees. Although each one is more fragrant than the last, they fail to attract the sequestered *ali'i wahine*.

Earlier in the story, as Lā'ieikawai descends from the upland forest to meet a potential husband, a series of bird calls announces her arrival: first the '*ō'ō*, then the '*alalā*, the '*elepaio*, the '*apapane*, and finally the '*i'iwipōlena*. The passage made me wonder, "What do these birds look like? What do they sound like?" I vaguely recalled these birds from words and pictures, but couldn't remember exactly what they looked like, never having seen any of them in real life. I referred to *Hawai'i's Birds*, by the Hawaii Audubon Society, to refresh my memory:

'Ō'ō. A black honeycreeper with a tuft of yellow feathers under its wing.

'Alalā. The Hawaiian crow.

'Elepaio. A chestnut-brown flycatcher with black and white markings.

'Apapane. A crimson honeycreeper with black wings and tail and white under its tail.

'I'iwipōlena. A bright vermilion honeycreeper with black wings and tail and a long, curved orange beak.

The book also revealed that only three of these five birds are still common in the forests of the Big Island: the *'elepaio*, the *'apapane*, and the *'i'iwipōlena*. The *'alalā* is rare and near extinction in the wild, found in only one small forest area on the

The understory of a healthy Hawaiian rain forest ecosystem is dense with shrubs, herbs, ferns, mosses, and other plants, and rich with insects; the tree canopy is primarily the realm of birds. This contrasts dramatically with rain forests of other places such as those of South America where the majority of ecological diversity is high in the canopy layer.

As a result, the challenges of preserving biological diversity in Hawai'i are unique. Our forests are highly susceptible to the impacts of animals and weeds. Animals disturb the forest floor by grazing, digging, and destroying delicate plants. They also clear the way for invasive plants. Alien weeds are often able to out-compete with native plants and can quickly grow tall, shading out whatever lives below. In order to protect remaining native forests, managers are forced to fence large areas and must constantly be on guard against new populations of invasive weeds and animals.

Photo by David Liittschwager and Susan Middleton

Kona Coast. The Hawai'i 'ō'ō, common in Kona as recently as 1892, is believed to be extinct. The Kaua'i 'ō'ō was last seen in the Alaka'i Swamp in 1973. A sighting of a single bird was reported on Maui in 1981.

According to Hawaiian historian David Malo (1793 to 1853), the 'ō'ō, the 'alalā, the 'elepaio, and the 'i'iwipōlena were caught as food (Malo, *Hawaiian Antiquities*, 1903). The feathers of the 'ō'ō, 'alalā, 'apapane, and 'i'iwipōlena were also used to make royal standards called *kāhili* and feather capes. The yellow feathers of undertail and flanks of the 'ō'ō were so special and prized that a feather cape made of them became a symbol of high rank. In *Lā'ieikawai*, Waka, as a demonstration of her great *mana* and as a symbol of the status of her foster child, is able to construct a whole house of 'ō'ō feathers. The house has an awe-inspiring, intimidating effect on all who see it.

Another reference, *A Field Guide to the Birds of Hawaii and the Tropical Pacific*, gives word-rich descriptions of the bird calls:

'Ō'ō. A loud, harsh oh-oh.

'Alalā. Highly varied, including a weird sounding kee-o-reek, a quiet kwahk and other short notes. In flight, often utters a loud but musical krra-a-ik, upslurred and somewhat modulated.

'Elepaio. Various calls include an up-slurred whistled wheet, a sharp keet, and a raspy chatter. The song is a loudly whistled e-le-PAI-o or chee-WHEE-o.

'Apapane. Incredibly varied calls and songs, including squeaks, whistles, rasping notes, clicking sounds, and melodic trills.

'I'iwipōlena. An almost infinitely varied repertoire of creaks, whistles, gurgles, and reedy notes often joined into a halting song.

Not many of us would be able to match the descriptions to actual sounds in the forest, but the words made me wish I could hear the calls and distinguish among them. H. Douglas Pratt's tape set *Voices of Hawai'i's Birds* includes recordings of the voices of the 'alala, the 'elepaio, and the 'āpapane.

The places we usually frequent in our daily lives, the high rises and subdivisions and shopping malls, are not the habitat of these birds. Where most of us live is dominated by a new imported landscape of ornamental and fruit trees from all over the world; the native birds evolved in a much different habitat, the Hawaiian forest.

above
Maui Creeper
Paroreomyza montana newtoni
opposite
Hawai'i Thrush
'Ōma'o
Myadestes obscurus

Two of Hawai'i's more common
forest bird species found in high
elevation forests, are shown
here singing.
Photos by Jack Jeffrey

Hawaiian Crow
'Alalā
Corvus hawaiiensis

The decline of the 'alalā is partly due to the introduction of cattle and the pasture land needed to feed them. Pasture grasses impeded growth of native shrubs, which are the primary food source for the 'alalā.

Today, there are no 'alalā left in the wild, but 45 birds are being bred in captivity, with the hope that they can be reintroduced in the wild.
Photo by Jack Jeffrey

Hawaiian Hawk
'Io
Buteo solitarius

Although formerly found on O'ahu, Moloka'i, and Kaua'i, today they remain only on the island of Hawai'i. 'Io hunt primarily in forested areas and only occasionally are seen over pastures or agricultural land.
Photo by Jack Jeffrey

In the 1890s Robert Cyril Layton Perkins, of the British Joint Committee for the Zoology of the Sandwich Islands, went in search of the mamo. *Perkins's diaries relate that a Hawaiian bird catcher took him "to the very tree in which it [Drepanis Pacifica] had been shot at the time when the 1830 flow was approaching Hilo. He [the bird catcher] was in the forest then, and a dozen were killed at that time. Whenever he has been with me, all the time as we go along he gives what is no doubt an exact imitation of the Mamo's call. . . . He never succeeded in getting a response to his call."*
(From Anita Manning, "The Sandwich Islands Committee, Bishop Museum, and R.C.L. Perkins: Cooperative Zoological Exploration and Publication," in *Occasional Papers,* Vol. 26, p. 12, May 1986, Bishop Museum.)

Seen here is possibly the last mamo, *on the hand of a Mr. Wolstenholm in 1891. He was an assistant to Henry C. Palmer, who was sent to Hawai'i by Sir Lionel Walter Rothschild to collect specimens for his private museum in England.*
Courtesy of Bishop Museum Archives

Those who occasionally hike in this forest would not be able to identify the birds or their calls without some training. When I was in school, we did not receive such training, studying instead mainly the flora and fauna of North America in our biology textbooks. Later, during my college years (the 1970s), when I hiked many of the valley and ridge trails of O'ahu, I hadn't learned to identify native forest birds and, thus, didn't look for them; even if I had heard one, I wouldn't have known it. Not that I would have been able to find them if I had looked: on this most urbanized of the islands, the *'elepaio* is "local and uncommon" and designated endangered by the U.S. Fish and Wildlife Service; the *'apapane* "declining," and the *'i'iwipōlena* "rare."

Moolelo o Pakaa a me Kuapakaa, published in 1902 by Moses K. Nakuina, introduces the reader to another ecosystem of the Hawaiian forest—the *wao koa*. Pāka'a is the *kahu iwikuamo'o*, or trusted attendant, of Keawenuia'umi, the ruling chief of Hawai'i. After Pāka'a's position in the royal court is usurped by two incompetent and malicious pretenders, he flees into exile on Moloka'i. When Keawenuia'umi begins to miss his *kahu pono'ī* and wants to find him and bring him back, his advisors tell him to go to the mountain forests to get trees to build canoes because his *kahu* is on another island. The *wao koa* provided the trees for canoe building. The success of this activity was dependent on the help of the forest spirits.

Keawenuia'umi's canoe builders are hindered by two birds who hover and chirp above each tree they select; but each tree turns out to be rotten. (The *'elepaio* pecking at a trunk is said to indicate that the tree is not good for canoe making because it is full of insects.) We find out that the birds are Pāka'a's *'aumākua*, and they are delaying the canoe builders until Pāka'a can prepare to host his *ali'i* and destroy his enemies. By the time the two birds are finally brought down by the famous archer of ancient Hawai'i, Pikoiaka'alalā, Pāka'a is ready. Of course, the birds are not destroyed—they are spirits: ". . . amazingly, when the kānaka searched for the birds, the bodies couldn't be found—the birds were never seen again at that place."

After the birds disappear, the *kāhuna kālai wa'a* are able to cut down enough tall, healthy trees suitable for making canoes *(koa kūpono)*, and his *kānaka* haul the rough-hewn trunks down to the shore for shaping.

While traditional Hawaiian stories like *Lā'ieikawai* and the one of Pāka'a and Kūapāka'a contain motifs similar to those found in European romance (love, lust,

deceit, jealousy, betrayal, revenge, justice, and so on), they offer the added benefit of teaching local readers about the place in which they live.

The stories provide us with a vision of the Hawaiian forest of the past and a benchmark of its health. In comparing the forest in the stories to what exists today, we can see what has been lost: the *ōʻō* probably extinct; the *ʻalalā* nearing extinction; the other birds uncommon, rare, or declining.

In the 16th century, when Keawenuiaʻumi needed a fleet of canoes, he found enough trees for his needs in the *wao koa*. Four centuries later, in 1991, when the canoe builders for the Polynesian Voyaging Society went looking for two koa trees large enough for the hulls of a double-hulled voyaging canoe, they were unable to find a single, healthy tree.

In the intervening centuries (mainly during the last two centuries), the forest area was reduced by logging and land clearing for cattle ranching and agricultural plantations, and, more recently, for subdivisions and shopping centers. Thirty-one species of birds have been lost. Even before that, during the thirteen-plus centuries between the arrival of native Hawaiians and that of Westerners, about fifty species of birds disappeared.

The contrast between past and present certainly suggests there is some work to be done to protect and care for what is left of the native forest and to restore it where possible. Various projects, some controversial, others not, have been proposed and implemented—from replanting native vegetation, to protecting habitats, to breeding endangered animals in captivity and reintroducing them into the wild.

To sustain such projects, a great deal of effort needs to go into education. The urban and suburban dwellers who make up most of Hawaiʻi's population today may have never been in a Hawaiian forest, may not be aware of what is there (or what was there). It is hard to encourage people to care for something they don't even know exists. What we need is collective memory of the past and an educational system that maintains this memory. Nainoa Thompson once shared with me a step-by-step approach he wanted to use to create an educational program aimed at motivating the community to care for our land and sea (*mālama* Hawaiʻi):

- Raising awareness of what is special and unique about Hawaiʻi
- Providing knowledge
- Building understanding and respect
- Caring for and protecting

Awareness, knowledge, and understanding can come, in part, from science, but students and the public also need to be introduced to the traditional stories, for their informational and their affective and spiritual values. They do not just provide knowledge and understanding, but instill a respect that comes from a spiritual understanding of the life of the land and sea.

These stories depict the forest as a place where human beings belong, where they interact with plants and animals. The stories identify forest spirits who can

be helpful to us: in addition to the *'i'iwi* and the *'elepaio*, we encounter the *pueo*, or owl; the canoe-building gods Kūmokuhāli'i, Kūpā'aike'e, Kūpulupulu, and Lea, or Hinaulu'ōhi'a; Laka, the forest and hula goddess; Maikohā , the *wauke* plant, used in kapa-making; Lonopūhā, a god of healing with medicinal plants and minerals; Kāne, in his *'ohe*, or bamboo, form; Kū, in his *'ulu*, or breadfruit, form; Kanaloa, in his *mai'a*, or banana, form; and many others.

In addition to reading scientific and traditional lore, our education about the forest should also include hiking, with guides to interpret what we see and experience. At the most advanced level, a person might engage in an art requiring the gathering of forest materials to produce musical instruments, adornments, canoes, houses, tools, weapons, cordage, bowls, mats, baskets, bark-cloth and dyes, food, and medicines. An integral part of the training is an understanding of how to gather conservatively, without damaging the health of the forest or offending its spirits. Acknowledged and respected, these spirits allow practitioners to enter and gather safely, without damaging the regenerative powers of the forest. This kind of trained interaction with plants creates a close bond between humans and the forest. People engaging in such activity realize that the perpetuation of their arts, their cultural traditions, and their health depends on the health of the forest and its inhabitants.

Education about what is special and unique about the forest would perhaps work better to protect and preserve it than merely fencing off the forest.

If we are introduced to traditional Hawaiian stories when we are relatively young, they become a part of our unconscious understanding of the place we live in, as imagery or vision. This kind of fundamental vision, planted and nurtured in our minds from childhood through story and experience, makes a difference in our adult behavior and actions. As long as this vision remains alive, the community will continue to try to protect and preserve what remains of the forest and to restore what was once there.

It would have been helpful to me if we had learned, as children, a simple protocol for entering the forest, perhaps a chant, like this prayer to Laka (*Hawaiian Drum Chants: Sounds of Power in Time*, Smithsonian Folkways, 1989), to acknowledge the spirits who might "malu e hō ē, clear the path of all hindrances," when shown the proper respect.

MELE PULE NO LAKA

Noho ana ke akua i ka nāhelehele
I ālai ʻia e ke kīʻohuʻohu, e ka ua koko
E nā kino malu i ka lani
Malu e hō ē
E hoʻoulu mai ana o Laka i kona mau kahu, ʻo mākou nō
ʻO mākou nō ā ē.

The gods dwell in the woodlands
Hidden away by the mist in the low-hanging, blood-red rainbow
O beings sheltered by the heavens
Clear our path of all hindrance
Inspire us o Laka and dwell on your altar.
Free us.

Altar to Laka with *lama* wood and forest foliage

Forest plants provide ceremonial materials for hula kahiko, *traditional Hawaiian dance.* Hula kahiko *is religious in nature and performed in the* hālau hula, *a structure consecrated to Laka, goddess of hula.*

Chants to the gods are directed to an altar, kuahu, *containing a log of the endemic* lama *wood (Diospyros sandwicensis). The* lama *represents Laka. Other deities are also represented on the altar by forest plants.*

SUNSET AT KA'ALA 🌿

Jolie R. Wanger

As an employee of the Natural Area Reserve System of the State of Hawai'i, it is my privilege to occasionally escort groups of people—teachers, students, and others—into some of the most pristine places left in the islands. Mt. Ka'ala is a favorite destination for me because of its remoteness and its grandeur—rising over 4,000 feet in the Wai'anae Range, Ka'ala is the highest point on O'ahu. Each group is different, but the experience is always emotional for me as I watch people encounter the native forest of Ka'ala for the first time.

One day in the fall of 2002, my co-worker Betsy Gagne and I took a group of Hawaiian language college students up Ka'ala. As a follow-up to their study of Hawaiian *mele*, their teacher, Puakea Nogelmeier, had asked that his students be allowed to visit this place celebrated in Hawaiian song. We met at the Hawaiian studies building of the University of Hawai'i. It was afternoon, a little late in the day to be heading off to Ka'ala, but the group wanted to be on the mountain for sunset.

During the drive across O'ahu and up the mountain from Waialua, I was struck by the politeness of this group of young people. Their manner was respectful, whether they were addressing Betsy or me, or each other. After ascending the long, narrow road accessible only by authorized vehicles, we reached the trailhead, and the students showed the same respect toward the place. At the gateway to Ka'ala Natural Area Reserve, the group first offered an *oli* asking permission from the forest for them to enter. We then proceeded through the gate and along the boardwalk. There was less conversation than with most groups. Instead, they expressed a subdued awe at seeing and hearing the names of the plants, many of which they knew from songs and chants.

When we reached the end of the boardwalk, we caught our first view of the Wai'anae Coast spread out below, just as the mist began slowly rolling in and the sun was almost on the horizon. Puakea led the group in singing the *mele* they had studied, which described Queen Emma ascending the valley towards the place where we now stood. The wind had picked up, the mist surrounded us, and night

opposite

Hesperomannia arbuscula

This endangered plant, related to the daisy family, is a member of a Hawaiian endemic genus. The pollinator is unknown and is likely extinct, as this unusual flower does not produce seeds. Propagation from cuttings and tissue culture has been attempted with no success.

Meanwhile, the number of plants decreased from twenty-four to twelve in the Wai'anae Mountains on O'ahu. Currently, a joint effort between Hawai'i's Division of Forestry and Wildlife, U.S. Fish and Wildlife, Honolulu Board of Water Supply, and U.S. Army Environmental has begun to reproduce these plants by air layers.

Photo by David Liittschwager and Susan Middleton

was coming on. In that moment, I too felt a renewed awe for this indescribable place.

On the way in I had walked in the rear, so as we headed back I became the leader. Behind me, the students shared flashlights in order to follow the boardwalk. But I preferred to feel my way along, relying on my night vision and instinct. Surprisingly, I didn't stumble; instead, I seemed to be floating along the path. Too soon, we reached the end of the boardwalk and the gate to the Reserve.

High on the side of the mountain, the night was already quite cold. But the group was not yet ready to leave this special place. I should have expected it: they had brought a huge spread of food, enough for twice our number, and we placed it on a bench looking out over Waialua.

After we had all shared the food, Puakea brought out his ukulele and began to take requests from the students. One by one, each took a turn performing a hula. Tirelessly, they continued dancing and singing for hours. The energy and joy seemed endless, and I was sure, as I stood and watched, that the mountain was gaining strength and sharing in the moment as these Hawaiian youth reconnected with her. The following are a sample of *mele* written for Ka'ala by Puakea's students:

KE PANE WĒKIU O KA'ALA

'O ke ahe a ka makani
Ke lawe mālie i ke kēhau
He 'ahu 'ae'ae pō'ai puni
No ke pane wēkiu o Ka'ala

The soft wafting breeze
Gently carries forth the mist
To serve as a silken cape, draping
The uppermost summit of Ka'ala

'O ke ala he nonolu ehu
Pili kua, pili alo, huhui
Hu'ihu'i ka 'ili i ke anu
Pumehana 'o loko o ka poli

The path is soft and moist
As we move in a close-knit cluster
The skin is chilled in the cold
Yet one's heart is pleasantly warmed

Kolowao ka ua o luna

The rain above crawls along through
    the uplands

Kokolo ke kupukupu o lalo
Anuhea ke 'ala 'ōhi'a

The kupukupu fern crawls about below
The scent of abundant 'ōhi'a is a cool, sweet
    perfume

'Ula wena i ka wai o Kaiona

The vapors of Kaiona cast a reddish glow

opposite

The boardwalk that leads through Ka'ala Bog ends at the edge of steep cliffs and a view of the Wai'anae (West O'ahu) coast below. Mount Ka'ala Natural Area Reserve is part of the broader Natural Area Reserves System (NARS), created to preserve and protect representative samples of unique Hawaiian biological ecosystems and geological formations.

Currently there are nineteen reserves on five islands, encompassing more than 109,000 acres of the state's most unique ecosystems. The NARS are home to rare plants and animals, many of which are near extinction. The reserves also protect some of the major watershed areas, which provide our vital sources of fresh water.

Photo by Franco Salmoiraghi

Huli aku, huli mai lau lapalapa
'Alohi i ke kau a ka maka
He makamaka ka pua lehua
No ka noe e moani mai nei

Kiele Akana-Gooch

Glossy lapalapa leaves dance to and fro
Bringing their sparkle to the eye
The lehua flowers are intimate friends
With the gentle caress of the fragrant mist

HE MELE NO KA'ALA

Hikiki'i ka 'ohu i ka piko o Ka'ala,
Ka 'a'ala kolopua o ka nae o uka,

Luluhe ka palai i ka nolu 'ehu,
Ehuehu ka liliko o ke alaula.

Miliani a kani kapakē ka lapalapa,

I ka welelau makani kōaheahe,
A he pālihi ka leo o ka manu,
I ke alo o nā kama hele.

Kau mai ke kapa ano o ka pōlehu,
Māhe a'e ka mali'o no'ū,

'Uhē kāua, mā'e'ele i ka pō,

Ka pūnohu māhea o ka lani.

Pukuku'i i ka makani konāhau,

Hau'oki ninipo kāua,
Hi'ipoli 'ia i ka wehi o Ka'ala,
He nani kamaha'o e hi'olani nei.

Kamaoli Kuwada

Mist reclines at Ka'ala's summit,
The sweet flower-laden perfume of the
    uplands
Velvety soft ferns droop, awash with dew,
The fading rays of daylight are misty and
    obscure.

The pitter-patter of the lapalapa is a soft
    caress,
In the fringes of the gently blowing breeze,
And the song of the birds a light touch,
On the face of the travelers.

Twilight's cloak of stillness descends,
As the last glimmers of the fragrant dusk
    dissipate,
You and I are chilled, numb in the cold
    of the evening,
In the misty moonlight of the heavens.

Nestling together against the icy nip of
    the breeze,
The two of us are drowsy and chilled,
Embraced in the bosom of Ka'ala,
An indescribable beauty reclining before us.

KA NANI O KAʻALA

I ke anu o ka ʻohu kau ahiahi
Wēwehi ka lehua i ka hune ua
Koʻū ka lehua papa, ka ʻāhihi o uka

E maliu mai i ka nani o Kaʻala

Kiliheʻa ka ʻopua i ke alaula
Kohu pua lehua o ka lani lā
Lehua maka kōnunu i ka wai
Kupuohi maila i ka nani o Kaʻala

Hulilī ka lau o ka lapalapa
ʻŌlapa i ke ahe lau makani
ʻO ia nō ʻoe ʻo ka ua liʻiliʻi
Hāwanawana i ka nani o Kaʻala

ʻĀhiahia ka mahina i ka ʻohu
ʻOhu kolo i ka makani konāhau
Mohala maila ka luakalailani
Māʻamaʻama i ka nani o Kaʻala

Kaʻa nehe aʻe nei ka hei ʻohuʻohu
A ʻimoʻimo nā hōkū lani lipo
I kumulipo no nā hanauna
Eō mai e ka nani o Kaʻala

Līhau Hannahs

ᎧᏃ

In the chill of the settling mist of evening
The lehua is adorned by droplets of rain
Drenched are the lehua papa and ʻāhihi of
    the uplands
Give heed to the beauty of Kaʻala

The clouds are stained by the sunset
Like lehua blossoms of the heavens
A lehua face round, nectar-laden
Flourishing in the beauty of Kaʻala

The leaves of the lapalapa shiver
Dancing in the touch of the breeze
Sounding like the gentlest of rains
Whispering of the beauty of Kaʻala

The moon is made faint by the mist
The mist swept along by the crisp wind
Night's glory unfolds as a lunar rainbow
Shining upon the beauty of Kaʻala

The cloak of the mist rolls along
And stars sparkle in heaven's deep
As a source for all generations
A call to the beauty of Kaʻala

Sunset at Kaʻala

KĀHELA I LUNA KE ALO O LANIHULI 🌿

Sam ʻOhukaniʻōhiʻa Gon III

Kāhela i luna ke alo o Lanihuli i ka makani

The face of Lanihuli is upturned in the wind

Ka makani hoʻohula kāwelu i ka pali ʻāhihi ē

The wind that sets to dancing the kāwelu grass on the cliffs covered by lehua ʻāhihi

Hihi kolo i uka ka maile o Nāpuʻumaiʻa

Densely tangled are the maile vines of Nāpuʻumaiʻa

Mai nā puʻu uluhe hiwa ka ʻōhiʻa hā

From the hills covered by sacred uluhe grows the ʻōhiʻa hā

Haʻalipolipo ka nahele ma uka o Waolani ē

So deep and dark are the forests upland of Waolani!

Haʻaniponipo i ke kāwaha maʻukele

Creating a yearning for an opening in the forest

Hāʻaleʻale i ka haliʻa aloha ē

And the heart is filled with intense aloha

Hihipeʻa ka nahele ma uka o Mālama Kī

The forest growth is entangled upland of Mālama Kī

Hōʻulaʻula ka papa i ka lehua aʻo Puna

The plains are reddened by the lehua blossoms of Puna

Kūmalolohia Puna i ka ua ʻAwa a ka Wahine

Puna relaxes in the ʻAwa rain of the Woman (Pele)

Hinehineʻula i ka ʻāpoho kele aʻo Pohoiki

As the Hinehineʻula moss sits in the damp depressions of Pohoiki

E Kūkaʻōhiʻakūmakua

O Kū of the ʻōhiʻa in the Kū makua wind

E Hinakauluhenuihihikoloiuka

O Hina great tangles of uluhe fern in the uplands

Kau mai nō ka ʻeliʻeli!

Intense awe descends on me!

Loloa aʻe ka lama aʻo Pākūōaku

So tall are the lama trees of Pākūōaku

ʻŌwela liko ka liko lau i ka pali

Bright glistening red are the leaf buds on the cliff face

Hina ʻole i ka hakuʻina pōhaku

Unfelled by the pelting boulders

Māui ʻia ke kumu pūkonakona

Although the strong trunk is bruised

Māuiui aku i ka nui manu

Asking again and again of the flocking birds

Pehea la ka papa ʻauwai o Olokuʻi lei i ka ʻohu?

How fares the water-channeled plateau of Olokuʻi wreathed in the mist?

Commentary

Since ancient times, Hawaiians have been weaving the imagery of native forest into their chants and dances. This *oli*—celebrating the forests with vignettes set in three different localities in the islands—is a modern expression of this same art. It takes three forested places in my experience and threads a set of images that play with place names, names of winds and rains, and the native species that live in these places, to express a bit about what draws me to dedicate myself to conservation. As in all works of Hawaiian poetry, there is the literal translation (accessible to all), then the symbolic translation (accessible to the learned), and the *kaona*, the hidden meanings known only by the author. The *kaona* and symbolism is reflected by the descriptions of the settings. For example, in the first vignette, the upturned face of Lanihuli in the wind is at once a depiction of pride at having climbed that tall peak (the companion to Kōnāhuanui, the tallest peak in the Koʻolau Range of Oʻahu). The *kāwelu* grass is symbolic of Nuʻuanu, as are the strong winds there, as any *kamaʻāina* of the island could tell you. Less well known, unless you are a fan of Hawaiian song, is the *lehua ʻāhihi*, a delicate and long-stemmed form of *ʻōhiʻa* that grows on Lanihuli. The first verse also alludes to the sacred nature of the *wao akua* (realm of the gods) that tradition holds lies in the forested upland. In Hawaiian thought, deep blue or green is a sure sign of such sacredness, and the word for this, *lipolipo*, alludes to the *Kumulipo*, the long chant of creation, in which the world and all life emerge out of deep darkness and deeper antiquity. The hill called Waolani is pointed to as the spot from which human beings originally sprang, and the hill and the theme of creation are linked in that one line. To have experienced such a place and stood in the forest there, how could the heart not be filled with aloha?

The second verse describes the tall *ʻōhiʻa* forests of lowland Puna in one of the remnants of the forest type, at Mālama Kī. The color of Puna is red, both from the blossoms of the *lehua*, and from the fires of Pele. Yet, Puna is also a place of serenity, when the drizzly *ʻawa* rains fall and bring moisture to the depressions in the lava under the forest canopy. The gods of the forest are Kū and his consort Hina, and tradition holds that if your intent is not good as you enter the forests of Puna, Hina, in the form of entangled masses of *uluhe* ferns, will surround you and ensure that you never leave! Anyone who has been lost in the trackless expanse of the island of Hawaiʻi can relate to how small and lost you can feel under those circumstances. It is as if a physical weight is placed on your shoulders!

The third and final verse takes you to the island of Molokaʻi, to the remote north shore and the highest sea cliffs in the world. One steep ridge there takes you from Wailau Valley up to the mist-shrouded plateau of Olokuʻi, surrounded by precipitous cliffs, and thus the last native forest region that has never seen non-native ungulates such as pigs or goats. The ridge to Olokuʻi is called Pākūōaku (Place of calling out), since from that high ridge, the voice would carry downward to the inhabitants on the shore, or to canoes on the ocean at the cliff base. As you climb the ridge, the forest goes from drier *lama* and *ʻōhiʻa* to the wet *ʻōhiʻa* forest of the summit. The trees on the cliff face are battered and scarred by the rocks and boulders that occasionally fall from the cliffs. The *lama* tree, in this case, is symbolic of the chanter, who cannot go to the top of the mountain (because to do so would cause harm to the delicate ecosystem there), but who looks nonetheless at that immaculate forest as a sign of hope for the future of all native forests in Hawaiʻi. "How fares Olokuʻi?" As long as the answer to this question is, "Olokuʻi remains untouched and purely native," then there is hope for native species and ecosystems in Hawaiʻi, and the native foundation for all Hawaiian culture stands secure.

GIVING BACK 🌿
Alani Apio

My father told me, "Take out something from your lunch that you really like." I took the orange out from the brown paper bag and held it up. "Now leave it on the wall." I did—and then I looked up at him. "You always give back. Leave something special for the gods."

I was probably about six years old when this first happened. We were hiking in Mākaha Valley and it was the early 70s. I'm pretty sure we were at Kāneʻākī Heiau, though we didn't know the name for it back then. At lunch, I ate my Spam musubi and drank a can of guava juice. I wished for the orange back. I don't remember what we were hiking for—maybe looking for old bottles, maybe gathering guavas for jam, maybe just looking around. My father liked hiking all over the Islands, and since I was the oldest, I always got to go with him. I didn't understand why we had to leave a favorite thing on the wall of the *heiau*—I only knew that we should always sacrifice something of value to a greater being or force. Dad is a man of few words, so it never occurred to me to ask him to explain.

I come from a family of fishermen, and by that age I already knew to throw the first fish back when we gathered in the nets from a round of *paʻipaʻi* fishing. The first fish, the one we were supposed to throw back, had to be a *good* one. A puffer or baby hammerhead didn't count. But no matter how big the fish was, no one ever hesitated—though my uncle sometimes let out a low, long whistle as he released a particularly huge *moi*. Like the orange left at the *heiau*, I knew to do it, but not why.

As I grew up, my father and I hiked together less and less. *Paka lōlō* started spreading, and we heard stories of booby traps and growers beating up people who came near their plots. "Keep Out" or "Kapu" signs went up in places where we used to walk freely. As for the places where we'd fished together, the reefs died, and so there was no point in going back. I think building the Reef Runway killed a lot of the fishing grounds around ʻEwa. Everything got covered with silt. By the early 80s, more and more people started coming to pick *limu*, but they had to go farther and farther out to find seaweed that used to be abundant when my father and I would

opposite

Two calabashes made by the author from kou (Cordia subcordata) *wood.*
Photo by Hal Lum

83

just pick from what rolled in with the surf. And the new *limu* pickers didn't just take what they needed: they carted off big burlap sacks to sell at the market. I didn't see them leave anything behind, even symbolically.

In college, my love for the ocean landed me a job catching tropical fish. To this day, my most beautiful memories are of the days I spent off Waiʻanae and the South Shore of Oʻahu gathering brilliant, tiny jewels of life from the reefs. My dive partner, who grew up in Chicago, would tell me, "Take what you can now, because tomorrow another diver will be here and *he'll* clean it out. Might as well we reap the rewards." They weren't food fish, I rationalized, and at that time I was the classic starving college student. It took about two years before the voice of my father finally broke through: just because someone else was going to rape the reef the next day didn't justify me doing it today.

After the fishing grounds were depleted, my father took up woodturning. He had inherited three ʻumeke, wooden calabashes, from his *tūtū*, and the pieces tantalized us. Could we make things as beautiful as our *kūpuna* had? He started turning pieces from whatever wood he came across. I was mesmerized by both the process and the products of his lathe. Once again we had a reason to return to the forests: now we needed wood.

Though most people think of koa when they think of Hawaiian bowls, the primary woods my Kānaka ancestors used for their food utensils were *kou* and *milo*. Both of these are lowland trees. They're not endemic, probably not indigenous either; theory suggests that the first migrants brought them here as seeds. But these woods are highly prized by artists and collectors alike. They are more rare than koa. Being lowland plants, most were cut down during all our shoreline development, and no one has planted them for commercial harvesting.

As luck would have it—or blessings, as I choose to believe—we found two incredible sources for *kou* and *milo*. No one else seemed to know they were growing in this place, or cared. In fact, the owners of one source considered the *kou* a nuisance because the trees constantly dropped seeds that clogged up lawnmowers, and the strong roots of the *kou* cracked the concrete foundations of the houses and broke the driveways. We offered to cut the trees down and haul them away in exchange for the wood. The owners were only too happy to have us do for free what used to cost them thousands of dollars. We never charged them for the work,

Apio

though we could have simply undercut the going rate for tree trimming. Gathering the wood was all that mattered. After a while, we started growing trees at my parents' house from seeds that we had collected when out harvesting.

Eventually our wood products got to be nice enough to sell. Soon I was taking large orders, and after about a year, I quit my first corporate job to be a full-time woodworker. Gradually, as we cut tree after tree to keep up with the orders, what had first appeared to be a lifetime supply of wood began to look clearly finite. We guarded our secret sources carefully, though we also gave wood away to other artists. My father and I donated pieces to non-profit groups, and still do. We have always given pieces away when it was *pololei*, the right thing to do, and always make a bowl for whoever has given us a tree. At Waipahu High, my father provided *kou* seedlings for planting.

When we were asked to be partners in a new co-op, Native Books and Beautiful Things, we jumped at the opportunity. By then, dad had retired from thirty-five years at Pearl Harbor and was turning full time. We needed even more wood, and we became ever more conscious about conserving natural resources and replacing what we used.

One day, we were out harvesting some *milo* trees when two DLNR officers walked up to us. They had guns at their sides. I was about fifteen feet up in a tree, chainsaw in hand, taking down limbs.

"Stop now and get out of the tree," the lead officer yelled. My father walked off and sat down. I turned off the chainsaw and climbed to the ground.

"What do you think you're doing?" the officer asked, clearly angry and ready to arrest us.

"Harvesting a dead *milo* tree before it's too rotten to be of any use," I answered. He looked hard at the tree. It was true: the bark had already fallen off and the outer sapwood was riddled with insect holes.

"Right now, we can still cut the sapwood away and use the clean heartwood. But you know, once a tree loses its bark, it's dead."

"This is conservation land," the officer said. "It's against the law to harvest on conservation land."

"We're Native Hawaiians exercising our right to collect natural resources for religious and cultural purposes," I answered. "Besides, officer, you can see the tree is dead. It's only going go to waste if we leave it here. Nothing here is native anymore. Even these trees aren't native—you know that." He looked at our neatly stacked piles of wood. The ends were dry and it was obvious that the tree was dead. I could tell by their faces and the names on their badges that the two officers were Kānaka like us.

"Go ahead, then. But get a permit next time. We'll tell the people who called in what's going on."

Although I have gotten permits for other areas, I never got one for that place. We took down a live tree later that afternoon. Over the years, we have taken down many live trees there—running into those particular officers was luck, or a blessing, as I view it. Over the years I have gone up there and planted *kou* and *kamani* seedlings, though nobody but my father knows. I always left trees behind, never clearing an area completely. I never cut the smaller trees and took care not to crush or smother the saplings that were all over the place. And although that land is in a conservation district, it's actually undeveloped Hawaiian Homelands' property. I figured, if we can't get a house (my father's on the list), can't we at least get some wood?

But I ask myself constantly, "Have I given enough back?"

What if all us Kānaka decide to collect fish from the reefs and koa from the forests? Would we be able to give enough back when taking even a little will wipe out the source? Why was it okay in my childhood, but not now? I'm still just trying to feed myself, but if I collect wood for free and then sell my woodwork for a profit, does that automatically make it wrong? If a lei maker collects *maile* to sell, is that wrong? Does it make a difference if that lei maker happens to be Kanaka?

Many people call my father and me for a donation or discount on our pieces, and we almost always give it to them. Will our generosity make a difference when we're arrested for illegal harvesting? How can the state encourage the arts of its native people, yet make it illegal for us to collect the resources needed to create them? Will generosity make a difference if we over-harvest the trees? What's the difference between a school of *akule* and a koa tree in this regard? Why can the fish in Hawaiian waters be depleted for profit by anyone—and without adequate regulation or enforcement? And even where there are fishing regulations, no one considers an honest fisherman a thief—but he's taking natural resources supposedly owned by all (or no one) and selling them for his personal gain. Who "owns" our natural resources? Who decides who can take what when? Where is the balance?

I'm no scientist; I don't know if what I've done over the years has hurt our forests or ocean resources irrevocably. I only know what my father told me—give back. I've always done that, although I know others don't even think of it. I'm not rich, but I live pretty well, and a good portion of that living has come through harvesting in our forests. So, I keep a ledger in my *na'au*, inside me, carved by my father, to make sure the scales are even. Trouble is, no one can see the ledger and it's obviously subjective. The truth is, if I thought too much about the complexities of the equations, I would give up. I just have to know that it feels *pololei*.

The truth is, the more humans we put into this finite island ecological system, the more of it we will invariably lose—both in quantity and quality. The truth is, we must regulate the use of these resources. And when we do that, the Kanaka culture is even more severely pressed to preserve and perpetuate itself.

We all know the truth at a deep level: we simply cannot have it all. In fifty years, when our grandchildren are trying to buy homes and there's no more open land, what will we tell them? When I take from our natural resources to survive, how much is enough, or too much, and who should decide?

HAWAI'ILOA ✻
Nainoa Thompson

When our ancestors built and sailed voyaging canoes, it required the labor and arts of the entire community, everyone working together—some collecting the materials in the forest, others weaving the sail, carving the hulls, lashing, preparing food for the voyage, or performing rituals to protect the crew at sea. So we thought that building a canoe of traditional materials would bring our entire community together, not just the sailors, but the crafts people, artists, chanters, dancers, and carvers. The Native Hawaiian Culture and Arts Program was set up to build not just a canoe, but a sense of community, by recreating Hawaiian culture.

We started in our koa forests and ended up finding that in the last 80 to 100 years, ninety percent of our koa trees have been cut down. The ecosystem that once supported this healthy forest is in trouble. We could not find a single koa tree that was big enough and healthy enough to build one hull of a canoe.

On our last weekend of the search, in the Kīlauea Forest Reserve, on the island of Hawai'i, we searched with a large team and found nothing. Everyone went back to work on Monday, but Tava Taupu and I stayed in the forest. We decided that Tuesday would be our last day. At that point I was very project oriented—we have a job, we've got to build a canoe—but inside I was sad and depressed by the difference between what I imagined our native forests to look like and what they actually looked like. All around us were alien species and ferns uprooted by feral pigs, introduced to Hawai'i in the 19th century. I saw a layer of banana poka vines twisting in the canopy from one tree to another, choking the trees.

"There's a fence line up ahead about a half mile," I told Tava. "I'll go upslope, and we'll work toward it together to cover more ground. We'll meet at the fence. If we don't find anything, that will be it."

Tava nodded and began moving forward. We knew that we were not going to find any trees, that the search was going to fail, but it was our last chance. When I saw Tava and he saw me, from that moment, we never spoke. We each knew the other had not found a tree. We did not even walk on the same side of the road.

opposite

Offerings are placed at the base of a koa tree before cutting it to build a canoe.
Photo by Franco Salmoiraghi

Tava walked behind me, as if we were repelled by each other. We were very depressed. We had not achieved what we so much wanted to achieve. But beyond that, I think the loss of the forest was eroding something inside of us.

There was another source of trees for Hawaiian canoes. We knew trees from the Pacific Northwest drifted to Hawai'i, and that our ancestors cherished them and built canoes from them. Herb Kane and I had talked about our project earlier with his old friend, Tlingit elder Judson Brown, who was chairman of the board of Sealaska, a timber corporation owned by Native Alaskans. Judson fully understood what we were trying to do. It was about reviving our culture, and he knew the trees were the tools for doing that. Without hesitation, he said, "We will give you trees for your canoe if you need them."

After we ended our search for koa trees, we called on Judson and Sealaska and gave them the specifications for the two trees we needed. They said they would search, and they did, for six weeks in the remotest parts of their forests in Alaska. Then they called us up and said, "We have the trees of your specifications. But we're not going to cut them down unless you come up here and tell us it's okay, because we believe that our people are connected to the natural environment, that the trees and the forests are family to our people. And we're not going to take the life of a family member unless we know this is what you want."

I was in charge of building a canoe. That was my narrow focus. But around this project were so many layers of values that I did not clearly see. I understood them, I felt them, but I did not see them as part of my responsibilities. I was thinking of deadlines and logistics. Judson gave me a new perspective based on the values of his elders; it's the kind of wisdom that we always seek from the older generation.

So we flew up to Alaska. We got a helicopter in Ketchikan and went west eighty miles to a remote forest on Shelikof Island. Our guide was Ernie Hillman, a forest manager for Sealaska. He had done his job. The trees were exactly what we asked for. But when he asked me, "Shall we cut these trees down?" I couldn't answer him. I didn't want to cut the trees down. They were too beautiful, too full of life. I began to weigh the value of our project against the value of the life of the trees. I was just too troubled. Everybody got real quiet. I couldn't explain myself. The trees were breathtaking—I had never seen trees like that before, giant evergreens. I began to sense Alaska's power. There was something so very different about it, something alluring. It was very spiritual, and that made me quiet and humble. The place was so wild, so clean and still, so natural. I began to face up to the reckless changes taking place in Hawai'i, especially on O'ahu. When I was a kid, I felt very lucky to be from here—and I still do—but the reefs in Maunalua Bay were still alive back then, and now they are dead. We got back on the helicopter, and no one talked. We flew back to Honolulu. The trees remained in the forest.

Something was wrong. I didn't know what it was. I talked to Auntie Agnes Cope and John Dominis Holt, our elders who were on the board of the Native Hawaiian Culture and Arts Program, which was supporting this project to build a canoe called *Hawai'iloa*. Why didn't I ask for the trees to be cut down? It was because by taking the trees out of Alaska, we were walking away from the pain and the destruction of our native Hawaiian forests. We could not take the life of a tree from another place unless we dealt with the environmental abuse in our own homeland. The answer was clear. Our elders told me, "You know what the answers are. To deal with the abuse here, you need to do something to renew our forests. Before you cut down somebody else's trees, you need to plant your own." So we started a program at Kamehameha Schools to plant koa trees, and we've planted over 11,000 koa seedlings, in hopes that in 100 years, we might have forests of trees for voyaging canoes.

At the planting, I remember grandchildren with grandparents, a big circle of people participating in healing the forest. It was a diverse group. There was a growing sense of community. What started as a project of artisans and people within the Hawaiian voyaging community now extended as far as Alaska.

This event brought closure to the search for koa trees by recognizing that we had a real problem in our land. Even though the planting was symbolic, we were contributing in a way that was sending the right kind of message to our communities about replacing abuse with renewal. This became a fundamental value that began to permeate all our decisions. It was the groundwork for what guides us today—*mālama* Hawai'i, taking care of Hawai'i, our special island home.

BRINGING DOWN THE WATER ✺

Eric Enos, with Gail Hovey

Water is . . .

philosophically, spiritually
water is sacred,
it is Kāne i ka wai ola, the life giving
    waters of Kāne.

Out in Waiʻanae especially—
and in places where there is not much water—
you really see it like blood,
like the blood in your body,
the koko.

Just as our bodies would die if we had no blood,
so the land would die if the water was gone.
The water on the land, the blood in our bodies
are the same.

It has to flow
as the blood in our bodies has to flow
the water on the land has to flow.
The constant cycle of renewal
just as new blood is constantly being reproduced
    and all these things the blood requires,
so does the water.

The rain and the water are life giving.
That's the sacredness.

✺

We did go onto the land many years ago,
a parcel of land in upper Waiʻanae Valley.
It's a long story. The land was ranched, and
    the water was

diverted, taken down, maybe a century ago,
    to the sugar plantations.
But prior to that it was land that was a living
    complex
a cultural complex and slowly we are
discovering the extent of that complex now
    with archaeology.

We went onto the land in
the summer of 1978
we brought the water
down from the diversion ditch,
the plantation diversion ditch—
nine hundred feet elevation is the entrance
    where the streams converged,
where Kaʻala Farm is about five hundred feet
    elevation—
we brought the water down one mile.
In the summer of 1978
the Waiʻanae Rap Center staff, community
    volunteers
and summer youth program participants
we ran the pipe.
By the end of summer
we had one mile of two inch PVC.
And we were clearing the land at that time at Kaʻala
and we planted our first taro patch.

It was very difficult because the land is rocky,
it's steep and going over stone walls, so . . .
There's no native plants,
only koa haole

opposite

Rain falling on kukui.
Photo by Masako Cordray

so we cut the koa haole,
just kind of try and cover the pipe with brush
as much as possible try cover,
trench it just a little bit,
just to try to keep it from the sun
so little bit of covering.
We brought it down.
And then we made our first loʻi kalo
and water first came back on the land at that point.

That was quite a moving experience
to see the water.
It comes from kind of a kukui nut grove,
where if you go up,
you go up about a mile above us.
At the farm itself it's very dry.
It's very arid.
It's hot.
You walk up a mile
and you're almost like in the back of Mānoa.
It's wet, it's cool.
Kukui nut groves and coffee
it has a sense of moisture
and so where the water came from is actually
    kind of lush
because the stream is pretty constant over there.
So bringing the water down from that kind of a
    little stream, rivulet,
which was wet and really kind of nice and cool
and coming down into an area that is totally dry
    and hot
and getting that cool water coming onto the land
on top of an ancient taro terrace,
that was quite an experience for us.

I can still remember us
when the first water came through the pipe
and just watching the water flow out of that pipe
and feeling its coolness
as we walked in it in the mud,
the cool mud.

And from there the loʻi just blossomed,
taro grew, ti leaves, bananas
and from there we just fitted in pipes and just
    started planting.
We just planted.
Cleared and planted,
cleared and planted as much as we could.
So it was pretty exciting times,
that summer and that year.
ALU LIKE helped us a lot, helped provide some
    of the youth labor.
The state and city had programs,
training programs,
there were ex-offenders programs,
variety of things and resources
to help us put the program together.
So those were our partners in the early days.

෧෨

We have to mention though
that the summer of 1978
when we did run the water,
the end of summer,
I remember we were working up there
and some enforcement agents came out and
    asked us
who's responsible.

It was State enforcement, DLNR.
Department of Land and Natural Resources
    Enforcement Agents.
They came out. We were out there working
and they came walking up the road in their
    uniforms and they said,

"Who's in charge?"
And being the director, the supervisor,
I said, "well I guess I am."

And they said, "Well there's a complaint
of illegal diversion of water in Wai'anae Valley."
So I says, "Okay. So what now?"

They says, "Well there's a complaint filed
and you need to follow up with this complaint.
You're in violation."

So, I called around and figured that
I should just go straight to the top, so I called
    the Land Board
and said I'd like to make a presentation
about this violation.

I remember meeting with Mose Kealoha,
    talked to him
about what we were doing. He was on the
    Land Board
and he was pretty sympathetic so he called
    Land Board's attorney
and I talked to them and I ended up
making a presentation to the Land Board,
    and I showed them
old maps of the land, explained our program.

We're a non-profit community program.
We're leasing the land from the state, working
    with alienated youth, using this water
which nobody else was using, it was already
    pumped out of the valley
and all I was doing was picking up the leakage,
    the surface runoff
which was not developable by the Board of
    Water Supply and

as they already had their systems in and the
    surface runoff, which is basically leakage,
that water was not water for them to utilize
    because surface runoff water is not potable.

So I presented all that
and what happened at the Land Board
took a look at the issues,
took a look at what we were doing
and they ruled that they would give us
    permission
to lay the pipe on state land.
It's all state land at the back of the valley.

However
when the pipe went into the stream,
it was outside of their jurisdiction.
They gave us permission to put our pipe
    on state land
however where it goes into the stream,
actually physically enters the stream,
then it's outside their jurisdiction.
So that was the situation.
We could use the land to lay our pipes out
but where the pipe went into the stream
the Land Board, what they said was
that they weren't quite sure
who owns the water.
And I guess that's the situation,
that the Water Commission today is
    struggling with,
yeah. You can own the pipe,
it's not the Board of Water Supply,
do they own the water?
It's like the Waiāhole Ditch, you know.
You can own the ditch
but who owns the water?

It's Honua,
is the stream that crosses the land at Ka'ala Farm.
Honua connects to Kānewai.
There's a few major feeder streams
that are part of the watershed
in upper Wai'anae Valley.
Wai'anae Kai is the name of the area
but Kānewai seems to be that main stream,
the water of Kāne.

❧

We've formed a committee, Mohala I Ka Wai,
a community group to look at the question
of water in and of itself
because we believe
all the valleys
are being threatened.
If we allow all of the water to be taken
out of the valley, drying up the source,
if we do that
our land's ability to cure itself
will be taken away.
The valley needs water,
the mountains need water,
the trees need water.
The role of the watershed—
when it rains, the winter rains—
it's like a sponge.

I am going to make the parallel.
If you have a table top and if you poured water
    on a flat table top
the water would spill out and just fall to the
    wayside,
just fall to the floor and get wasted.
But if you have a table top,

if you had a little barrier along the edges of the
    table top
and you filled it up with rocks and greenery,
    and moss
and you poured water on it you could end up
    having a reservoir of water.
And if you kept it covered with green material
    or mulch or moss,
that water would probably stay there for months
    and months and months.
You know, the water would stay there
and if you wanted to get water you would be
    able to get water from there.

So that's why the upland forest,
the Wao Akua, Wao Kanaka
are very important
to have this groundcover of native trees,
and second level plants,
the shrubs to be groundcovers.

That is the ecological conservatory of water

like dew,
like the rain,
like a reservoir,
natural areas that recharge
our groundwater. It's critical
that we have this green biomass. If we cut it,
we create a desert. Inability of the land to hold
    the water,
that's why you have places like desertification.
    Overgrazing,
springs dried up and they allowed cattle
    unchecked. It wiped out
the watersheds and springs dried up. So the
    forestry in Hawai'i was actually

connected to the sugar industry because sugar,
  who depended upon water, saw the impact
of cattle going up into the watersheds, denuding
  the forests, and found that their springs and
  streams were drying up
and so they made the connection.

You would think that's such an obvious
connection but it was out of greed
and tunnel vision that people just didn't see
the connection,
and allowed the overgrazing,
and unfortunately it's a problem
that is shared even among our own leadership.
So allowed the forests to be depleted,
the sandalwood trade and the burning of our
  native forests
to get at the sandalwood.
Incredible environmental damage was done.

❦

We are understanding the concept of Wao Akua,
Wao Akua.
Those are the upper reaches.
Those are the areas
where the most rare and precious plants are
  and trees
and there are the forested areas,
the places where it's almost mystical
and these were the realm of the gods.

These are your primary watershed retention
  areas.
Even traditionally there were areas that you
  only went in
for a purpose,

to gather certain medicines,
to give homage to Kāne.
So it was an area that you just didn't tread on
and you went there very specific.
Wao Akua.
It's your most beautiful forest,
where your native plants live.
It's the realm of your ancestors in a sense,
your ancestral akua, Kāne.
And it feels sacred, even in going there.

And adjacent to that are areas we call
Wao Kanaka.
These were the upper reaches where
you could grow your 'awa,
you could grow your banana,
you could grow your plants, even your taro,
that you could use.
But it depended upon the Wao Akua,
the moisture.
It's like your living watersheds,
that's your Wao Akua.
Next to it is your wao kanaka
and the system in Wai'anae,
actually the system of land use in Wai'anae
is reversed.

You think of the ahupua'a.
You think of water coming from the mountains,
which it does in all ahupua'a.
However in a lot of other kinds of ahupua'a,
the taro lands were down low,
like in Waipi'o,
like in Hanalei,
like in Waikīkī.
The upper reached areas were your watersheds

and the streams brought the water down
to the lowlands where the huge taro fields were.

But in the Wai'anae Mountains
because there was limited water, the taro lands
    were up high
in the wao kanaka areas, and that's why we
    have our lo'i in the uplands.
It's very rocky.
But it's hilled terraces.

And that's where the kalo was grown,
the mai'a,
your lā'ī,
ti leaves,
your 'awa,
even up higher.
Usually your 'awa is right on the edge of the
    Wao Akua.
Places like that.

Your olonā that came from your Wao Akua.
Some of your medicinal plants,
your dye plants.
There were emergency areas
where plants were planted for times of famine.
So these were stashed away,
like banana and taro.

There's your kula land,
which is your midland,
your grasslands, kula land
which is more adaptive for sweet potato,
'uala.
And then your coastal lands
which is the land of the limu
and the ma'o,
your milo.
These are your coastal areas.
That is where your fishing areas were.
So those were the basic land divisions.

❧

In the mo'olelo, in the chants,
there are chants that talk about changing
    weather.
Every so many years you would have a shift.
You'd have different limu growing
and when the limu grew it would signal the
    coming
of a different kind of wind that brought drought
    and dryness.
And so when the limu would grow, the turtles
    would come in and eat that limu.
That signifies a change.
Now that limu growth is, we think, connected
to temperatures of water, the sea.
Today we call that El Niño.

Over the years,
over the thousands of years that Polynesians
    and their ancestors,
being people of the sea and having studied
    this . . .
I mean you're talking about a couple of thousand
    years at least.
Their scientists working, two or three thousand
    years.
These ancestors, our ancestors
who were dependent upon the sea and coastal
    lands,
they observed these things.
They could see these patterns.
But we see it in the chants on Moloka'i
from Kumu Hula John Ka'imikaua
that talked about when this wind would come
and this limu would come and would signal
    them to redo their planting.
A period of drought was coming,
a period of drought.
It might last anywhere from three to five years,
a period of drought.
And when that happened
they knew that they would have to redo their
    systems,
would have to grow a different kind of taro
that was more drought resistant.
You have to change your taro fields to sweet
    potato,
gear up for sweet potato,
plant a lot of sweet potato
so you'd have a lot of the pulapula, the cuttings.
And then you would have to do mass planting.
You would be depending upon sweet potato.
The taro would not be abundant.

opposite

Lo'i kalo *at Ka'ala Farm, with the
Wai'anae Mountains in the background.*
Photo by Franco Salmoiraghi

And this they learned.
Because famine,
the memory of famine
that was linked up to other cycles of weather
and cycles of creatures and animals and seaweed,
that signaled different changes.
The names of the winds
and the kind of a wind that came from one
    direction,
the drying up of the land and the changing . . .
So all these things were observed
and they are found today in certain chants that
    were handed down.

ℰ

For us to do our work,
I think it's first of all,
it's awareness
and getting the idea of water conservation
and the watershed
out of the political,
strictly strictly—
when I say political
I'm talking the worst scenario of political
where you're only trying for today—
look at my needs now and
only my back yard and
don't worry about somebody else's.
To really take a look at the long term impacts
    of what we do and long term planning
    and education of how we're going
    to conserve water.
How are we going to create a time of lessening
    dependency
on our natural resources, the depletion of those
    natural resources?

How are we going to be building and construct-
    ing things
in our homes and our plants along different
    lines of thinking?
And that takes a shift,
a shift in thinking.
But before that has to happen
we need to be aware that it's coming.

And the Waiāhole water is a perfect example of,
"Well, let's use Waiāhole water now and we need
    it for development of the ʻEwa Plain."

Well, okay, if we do that
then ten years from now or even less
we will be with the situation
where there'll be no water for any further growth.
We've already depleted the Waiāhole bank of
    water.
And now we're back to square one, we're in
    bigger trouble
because water levels,
dangerously,
underground water
reservoirs of water
are reusing water faster
than nature puts water back.
When that happens,
big trouble.
And that is where getting facts,
getting information,
getting people to own up to what's happening
    and saying,
better to stop now
and force decision makers
and force education
that people realize

we are in big trouble,
our children will be in big trouble.

Hālawa shaft,
you go to the Hālawa shaft water tunnel,
you will see the water levels for the past fifty years.
Go up to the Hālawa shaft.
When they first built that shaft, in December—
well they were building it December 6th, 1941.
      They were building that Hālawa shaft.
And that is the source of urban Honolulu's water,
huge reservoir of water.
December 7th they had to shut down.
But right after that they finished completion
      of the Hālawa water tunnels.
And you will see, that is the actual level of
      ground water,
of ground water.
And you will see what the ground water level was.
They have it marked in 1941.
You'll see the level in 1945;
you'll see the level of 1955;
you'll see the level of 1966;
and you can see it, where they first went there
and you can actually see it,
where that level was to where it is now today.
And now today it's way down.
It's an actual tunnel. And that is your ground
      water.
And if that doesn't tell you something.

Water has been falling on these islands
for thousands and millions of years.
When you think of geologic time vs. human
      time—
humans, it's like we've been here all the time.

In Western religions the humans are the center
      of the universe
we are made in God's image and all that.
But in geologic time you know
we're like a snap of a finger in a day.
That's human time.

So we better start dealing with this issue now.
Worry about it now while we still have it.
The time for action, to do something,
is now,
while we still have time,
although it's already at dangerous levels.

Like we said,
It has to flow.

Our bodies would die if we had no blood,
so the land would die if the water was gone.

The rain and the water are life giving.
That's its sacredness

As the blood in our bodies has to flow,
the water on the land has to flow.
The water on the land, the blood in our bodies
are the same.

HONOULIULI ✍

Anne Nanea Kahiwahiwa Rosa

Kilakila nā mauna o Waiʻanae
Kamahaʻo ka ʻUlalena aʻo Kaʻala
ʻOmaliō a momona ke kula aʻo ʻEwa
ʻEia Honouliuli, ka ʻāina, ka wai
Pā ka lā i ka malu o Puʻuloa
Ka home pana o Kānekuaʻana

E nānā Puʻuokapolei i ka lā kau
Hōʻikaika ka lā i ka wā Makaliʻi
Hoʻōla ka ua i ka wā Hoʻoilo
Uakea noho ana i Palikea
Noho ma Pōhākea a ʻike Hawaiʻi
ʻAʻala ʻiliahi ma ʻEkahanui

ʻŌmaʻo nā kāhili ʻo Kaluaʻā
Kolohe ka mele ʻo ka ʻelepaio
E lohe i ke kani oe o nā pūpū
Ka leo nahenahe o Puʻu Hāpapa
Nā pūpū kuahiwi liko i na pali
Lei pūpū a nā kumu lāʻau

E lupalupa nā mea maoli makamae
I Honouliuli ka puʻuhonua ʻōiwi.

Majestic are the mountains of Waiʻanae
The ʻUlalena rain of Kaʻala amazes
Broad and fertile are the plains of ʻEwa
Here is Honouliuli, the land, the water
The sun shines on the calm of Puʻuloa (Pearl Harbor)
The celebrated ancient home of Kānekuaʻana

opposite

Cyanea pinnatifida *is now extinct in the wild. The last known plant occurring naturally died in 2001. However, the plant was in the Tissue Culture/Micro-propagation Laboratory at Lyon Arboretum and currently new plants are being outplanted in the Honouliuli Preserve, a 3,692-acre forest preserve leased to the Nature Conservancy–Hawaii (TNC). As stewards of this land, TNC is attempting to restore remnant native ecosystems and to provide a place for learning and stewardship for residents of Oʻahu.*

Photo by David Liittschwager and Susan Middleton

Look at Puʻuokapolei as the sun comes to rest
The sun strengthens in the season of Makaliʻi (summer)
The rains heal in the season of Hoʻoilo (winter)
Uakea (white misty rain) dwells at Palikea
Sit on Pōhākea and see Hawaiʻi
Fragrant is the sandalwood at ʻEkahanui

Green are the kāhili of Kaluaʻā
The song of the ʻelepaio is rascally
Listen to the singing of the shells
The sweet voice of Puʻu Hāpapa
The shining shells on the cliffs
A lei of shells adorning the trees

Flourish, precious natives
In Honouliuli the native sanctuary.

Mele Honouliuli: Sharing Some Kaona

This *mele* celebrates the history, the natural beauty, and the native inhabitants of Honouliuli. It starts by looking to the majestic mountains of Waiʻanae. It then speaks of the ʻUlalena rain, a rain of Kaʻala that appears reddish. As the very male image of the high mountains contrasts with the female image of the broad and fertile ʻEwa plain, there is a duality. Honouliuli *ahupuaʻa* runs from the top of the Waiʻanaes down to Pearl Harbor (Puʻuloa). Puʻuloa is the ancient home of Kāne-kuaʻana , an *akua moʻo* who guarded the people of this area. When Kānekuaʻana was pleased with her descendants, fish and shellfish were abundant in Puʻuloa. The paradox of the sun shining ("Pā ka lā") on the calm ("malu"), dark waters of Puʻu-loa reflects on the times of both peace and war that this body of water has seen.

The second verse says to look at Puʻuokapolei as the sun comes to rest. Puʻu-okapolei is a hill that was used by Hawaiian astronomers as a reference for the set-ting sun's position. When looking toward Puʻuokapolei from a distant location, in the season of Makaliʻi (dry season) the sun would set to the north of the *puʻu*, and in the season of Hoʻoilo (wet season) the sun would set to the south of the *puʻu*. The sun strengthens in the season of Makaliʻi, and the rains heal in the season of Hoʻoilo. Palikea is often covered in mist, clouds, and a white misty rain, Uakea. Sitting on the top of Pōhākea and seeing Hawaiʻi Island was what Hiʻiaka did. From Pōhākea, Hiʻiaka saw her forests burning because her sister Pele had sent her lava flows into them, killing Hiʻiaka's beloved friend Hōpoe. ʻAʻala ʻiliahi, the fragrance of the ʻiliahi, in ʻEkahanui is another forest fire reference. It recalls the time when forests were burned in order to harvest sandalwood. After the burning, the scent of sandalwood could be detected, and the heartwood, undamaged by the fires, could be collected for trade with Asia. Another meaning for the sweet fragrance of the ʻiliahi is hope that one day the sandalwood will again flourish in ʻEkahanui.

"Ōmaʻo nā kāhili ʻo Kaluaʻā" speaks of the green feather standards that guard Kaluaʻā. These green *kāhili* are references to the lobelia plants, which grow with long stalks and abundant leaves at their tops, as well as to the ti plants, which also have a kāhili-like form. The *ʻelepaio* makes its home here, and it sings its *kolohe* (rascally) song to attract a mate. "Listen to the singing of the shells"—*"ke kani oe o nā pūpū,"* plays on one of the names for land snails, which is *pūpū kani oe.* Puʻu Hāpapa is a peak at the northern end of Honolulu; it is a last sanctuary for varieties of native snails. The sweet voice of Puʻu Hāpapa is the singing of these snails. The shining shells on the cliffs, *nā pūpū liko i nā pali. Liko,* meaning to shine, is also the word for the bud on the *ʻōhiʻa lehua* tree, so the snails shine, but they are also like buds of the *lehua.* The shells are like lei adorning the trees.

The *hui,* or chorus, of this *mele* repeats words of love and encouragement: "flourish, precious natives, in Honouliuli, the native sanctuary."

> *E lupalupa nā mea maoli makamae*
> *I Honouliuli ka puʻuhonua ʻōiwi.*

BLUE HAWAI'I: CONSERVATION IN PARADISE ✺
Vickie Caraway

It was hot, no doubt about that. After all, it was about 1 P.M. and we were searching for Hawaiian violets in a lava field near Kona, just sixty miles shy of the southernmost point of the United States. Marie Bruegmann, a botanist for the U.S. Fish and Wildlife Service (USFWS), gave a whoop. She had found two more mature plants of *aupaka*, the common name for *Isodendrion pyrifolium*, a woody shrub in the Violet family. Watching every step, I proceeded carefully to avoid twisting an ankle in the *'a'a*, the rough, uneven lava characterizing the substrate where this plant is found. Lisa Hadway, a Natural Area Reserve Biologist working with the Kona Dryland Forest Group, had also found two small seedlings of this plant.

"Wow, the world's population of this plant is actually twenty percent larger than we thought," I said. "We have ten mature plants left—not just the eight in the other location."

Conservation in Hawai'i is challenging. The USFWS and the state of Hawai'i list 282 plant species as endangered, ten as threatened, and forty-two as candidate species. Another 252 "species of concern" warrant listing, but many have already disappeared from their historical ranges. If you add to those numbers the 600 rare plant species and close to 100 documented extinctions, the total puts the entire Hawaiian flora—approximately 1,200 species—at risk. Without the participation of local and international botanical gardens, the outlook would be even grimmer than it is.

One plant that would definitely be extinct without the effort of Waimea Arboretum is *Kokia cookei*. Three of the four species of this hibiscus family genus, unique to Hawai'i, are endangered, and the fourth is extinct. Originally found only in an arid region of the island of Moloka'i, the *K. cookei* tree is difficult to propagate due to the lack of viable seeds. The last remaining tree was killed by a brush fire in 1978, just after Keith Wooliams, horticulturist and past director at Waimea Arboretum, successfully grafted a slip onto another *Kokia*. All existing plants of this species originate from this individual and survive only marginally as grafts on *Kokia*

opposite

Kokia cookei

Photo by David Liittschwager and Susan Middleton

drynarioides, an endangered species itself. However, high hopes ride on the efforts of Nellie Sugii, conservation officer at Lyon Arboretum. In 2002 Nellie obtained immature seeds of *K. cookei* from David On, director at Waimea Botanical Garden, and succeeded in establishing three seedlings in tissue culture in her micropropagation lab at Lyon.

Kokia cookei is included in Hawai'i's Genetic Safety Net List, a creation of the Hawai'i Rare Plant Restoration Group and the Center for Plant Conservation, Hawai'i office. About ten years ago this informal group of twenty-five government and private conservation partners chose to focus their efforts on the most critically endangered plant species in Hawai'i. Only plants with twenty or fewer individuals remaining in the wild or with fifty plants or fewer remaining in a single wild population qualified for inclusion on the Genetic Safety Net List. The 140 taxa currently on the list are a focus of Kaua'i's National Tropical Botanical Gardens conservation program. With funding from private sources and USFWS, staff member Steve Perlman, with contracted assistance from Ken Wood, will monitor and collect these critically endangered plants, a first step toward reestablishing them in secure areas of their habitats.

The dryland forest habitat of *Abutilon menziesii*, an endangered plant in the hibiscus family, is threatened by Honolulu's urban sprawl. To offset this threat, Honolulu Botanical Gardens is assisting Hawai'i's Division of Forestry and Wildlife in establishing a genetically representative population of the O'ahu "pink 'ilima" within Koko Crater Botanical Garden. With 450 to 500 individuals remaining in the wild, *Abutilon menziesii* is fairly common for a Hawaiian endangered plant. Horticulturists at Honolulu Botanical Gardens are demonstrating that an endangered species can become genetically viable and reproductive with skillful management.

Plant conservation in Hawai'i is helped by conservation programs all over the world. Dr. David Bramwell of the Jardin Botanico Canario, in Spain's Canary Islands, discussed the Hawaiian palm *Pritchardia munroi* at an island biodiversity session at the World Botanic Gardens Congress, in Asheville, North Carolina. This palm is well established in their garden and produces numerous seeds. In Hawai'i, only two wild individuals of this endemic fan palm remain in one small gulch on Moloka'i. While *Pritchardia* grows in many Hawaiian gardens, if more than one

Caraway

species is present, the seeds are likely to be hybrids because *Pritchardia* species hybridize readily. This is not the case with seeds from Jardin Botanico Canario, whose collections contain a single *Pritchardia* species *P. munroi*, a boost for conservation efforts in Hawaiʻi from an unexpected source.

Because conservation in Hawaiʻi is so challenging, the successes are that much sweeter. In her micropropagation lab, Nellie Sugii has successfully germinated about 200 immature seeds of the *aupaka* from the Kona dryland forest. With a little luck, most of these plants will survive the move from agar-base tissue culture medium to potting soil. Then, after outplanting many of the seedlings, a genetic repository will be established at Amy Greenwell Ethnobotanical Garden, in Kona, as a seed source for future reintroduction projects. The good news is that the *aupaka* produces many viable seeds—all of which will be needed to outplant this species in the many places it was previously established—on Niʻihau, Oʻahu, Molokaʻi, Maui, and Lānaʻi, as well as Hawaiʻi. Hopefully, within the next ten to twenty years, we can establish the *Isodendrion*, *Kokia*, *Abutilon*, and *Pritchardia* in their former ranges in the Hawaiian Island chain.

இ

The coconut wireless spreads the word like wildfire in the botanical community. "Is it true? I heard that *Cyanea truncata* was found in the Koʻolau Mountains again. Where is it? How many are there? Is it in flower? Does it have seeds?"

A small shrub in the *Campanulaceace* family (the lobelia/bellflower family), *Cyanea truncata* has only been collected twice in Hawaiʻi since 1931. No one knows if these plants were ever common. The two-to-three-inch, curved, tube-shaped flower ranges from white to bright magenta, or a combination of stripes of these colors—not the sort of flower that is easily overlooked. Recently rediscovered and located by Joel Lau, the botanical expert with Hawaiʻi Natural Heritage Program, the plant was precariously hanging by three roots on a steep, wet bank in a stream and just beginning its blooming season. Quickly a biweekly monitoring schedule was set up by enthusiastic botanists to check for seed production.

The excitement caused by the rediscovery of this plant is indicative of the worldwide interest in this group of plants. Hawaiʻi has 110 woody species in the lobelia family that are not found elsewhere in the world. Dr. William Hillebrand, author of the 1888 *Flora of the Hawaiian Islands*, was correct when he stated that these plants are the "peculiar pride of our flora." The blooms of this group range from delicate to fleshy with white, pink, red, green, yellow, and almost black flowers. Many species evolved fleshy embellishments like warts, barbs, spines, and deeply furrowed ridges. Some are palm-like, growing as tall as forty feet; others are multi-branched, resembling a candelabra; still others stayed small, clinging to steep, dry ridges and resembling a cabbage plant on a stick. All this variety evolved from only four to five seeds introduced to Hawai'i. It is interesting to note that while the lobelias evolved, a family of birds called the honeycreepers evolved in conjunction with them. A lobelia might evolve a flower shape that exactly fit the bill of a specific bird, assuring a food source for the bird and a pollinator for the plant. This kind of coevolution works great for both organisms. However, due to external factors, there is a problem with this evolutionary pact: at least thirty bird and over 100 plant species are now extinct in Hawai'i.

Like other Hawaiian plants, *Cyanea truncata* is extremely difficult to reintroduce into the wild. No one knows what its natural pollinator was, if the pollinator still survives, or if it has been replaced. After a specimen was discovered, the main question was whether it would produce seeds. After several trips into the gulch, fruit was finally found, but most had been eaten by insects. The two remaining fruit were collected and sent to Nellie Sugii at Lyon Arboretum's Micropropagation Lab. Luckily, one of the fruit had viable seeds and Sugii has produced over 200 seedlings in tissue culture. Phase one is accomplished: we have plant material! Phase two and three will be to successfully transplant the seedlings into potting soil and find an outplanting site that is safe from feral ungulates and alien weeds. Meanwhile the last known *Cyanea truncata* died. Conservation in Hawai'i is never easy!

Note: Since this book was first published in late 2003, there has been an exciting turn of events for *Cyanea truncata*. Botanist Joel Lau discovered a new natural population of three individuals in a Windward O'ahu valley. This population was subsequently fenced with permission of the landowner to protect it from damage by feral pigs. In addition, clones that were growing at Lyon Arboretum were outplanted and six individuals are still alive.

THE PŪ ʻOLĒʻOLĒ BLOWS AND ʻAWA IS POURED 🌀

A. C. Medeiros

opposite
ʻIliahi
Hawaiian Sandalwood
Auwahi, Maui

"The thought shared among many kūpuna and Hawaiian people today—E mālama i ka ʻāina iā ʻoe (Care for the land, and the land, in turn, shall care for you)—is one that is centuries old and is rooted in the spirituality of the Hawaiian people."
KEPĀ MALY

Photo by David Liittschwager and Susan Middleton

Past the little town of ʻUlupalakua and the tiny but gracious headquarters of ʻUlupalakua Ranch, on the leeward flanks of Haleakalā Volcano, begin in earnest lava fields that continue for another twenty or so miles until Kaupō district. To most who pass this way, *kapu* to rental cars, the lava seems barren and like a moonscape, formidable, almost hostile, and seemingly incapable of supporting life of any kind. Most are shocked to find out that these lava flows support some of Hawaiʻi's richest forests, the source of much of the material culture of the ancient Hawaiians—the Hawaiian dryland forests.

To those who pass through only once, their memories recall buffeting winds and torturously pitted roads winding through stretches of twisted lava and rocky ridges. But to those who know this country better, each of the *ahupuaʻa* (wedge-shaped land districts) that make up southern Haleakalā is deeply unique. To botanists, some of these *ahupuaʻa* names have acquired near legendary status, Kanaio, Lualaʻilua, Kepuni, Alena, Auwahi. This is due to the turn-of-the-century explorations of early Hawaiian botanists like Charles N. Forbes, of the Bernice P. Bishop Museum, and the renowned Joseph Rock, of the then College of Hawaiʻi (now the University of Hawaiʻi at Mānoa). Rock singled out the Auwahi District, on Haleakalā, and the Puʻuwaʻawaʻa District of the Big Island, as the richest botanical regions in the territory, with more tree species than any Hawaiian rain forest. Of the fifty-odd species of rare Hawaiian trees found here, forty-one species had specific Hawaiian ethnobotanical uses; nineteen of these had medicinal uses, thirteen were used in making specific tools, thirteen had uses in canoe construction, eight were used in kapa making, eight to make dyes ranging from pink to blue to a rich yellow-orange. At least seven of the trees have spiritual significance and were used religiously. Miscellaneous uses ranged from fireworks, to birdlime, to a fish narcotizing agent.

Since days of old, however, Auwahi has been greatly transformed by burning, grazing, and the invasion by non-native plant species. As a result, much of the original native understory at Auwahi has been replaced by a thick, smothering green mat of aggressive African Kikuyu grass, introduced as cattle forage. To many, Auwahi is known as a "museum forest." Though ancient, majestic trees of nearly every Hawaiian dryland species can be found there, most species have no seedlings and have had none for the past 50 to 100 years. Just like a museum filled with artifacts, these forests, in one sense, are no longer living, but just persisting in a type of shadow state, one windstorm away from becoming a pasture. By examining sub-fossil bones, we now know that these dryland forests at one time supported a tremendously diverse community of Hawaiian birds, from giant flightless geese (*moa nalo*) to the loud, sweet-singing, yellow and black honeyeaters. Now, except for the light twittering of white-eyes and occasional mynah squawk, the forests are quiet as a museum.

As a local boy from Kāneʻohe, Oʻahu, I came to know and love Hawaiian plants. I read Joseph Rock's often-poetic descriptions of these Hawaiian treasures of incomparable value growing at Auwahi, a far-off forest on Maui, and was deeply moved by them. Later, as a biologist, my dreams came alive when I had a chance not only to visit these areas but also to participate in efforts to save them.

Dreams wouldn't have gone farther than the first site visit without the complete empathy and support of the landowners, the Erdman family of ʻUlupalakua Ranch. First Pardee Erdman, and now his son Sumner, have always made one thing clear— "Let's see if we can run an honest, productive business and yet at the same time, do the right thing." This unflagging ethic of giving back to the land and community that supports them has been the precipitate for a multi-agency collaboration dedicated to protecting and restoring the superb Auwahi forests. Throughout all our years out there, the Erdmans have encouraged biologists to come and try to bring life back to Auwahi forest. For this, they deserve our most sincere *mahalo loa*.

Sponsored first by the U.S. Fish and Wildlife Service and now by U.S. Geological Survey, the U.S. Soil and Conservation Service, Maui County Water Department, and Haleakalā National Park, these efforts have evolved over the years into the construction of a ten-acre exclosure, from which invasive weeds were removed. Over two years, our team built a greenhouse at ranch headquarters and started gathering and germinating seeds of Auwahi's rare trees. By late 1999, we had about 2,500 seedlings ready to be outplanted. Based on five decades of monthly rainfall records, we selected the first week of January 2000 as the date most likely to receive winter rainfall. However, at the time of this project's inception, we had entered without

knowing it into two El Niño drought years—the driest two years ever recorded at 'Ulupalakua were just about to occur, back to back. (In spite of the severe ongoing drought, the trees have had a seventy-five percent survival rate, versus a ten to thirty percent predicted survival rate, and the project is considered a great success.)

It had been a busy three weeks of planning, logistics, and coordination before the actual outplanting. Everything was coming together well, but I knew one thing still needed to be done. Before starting a big task into uncharted territory, Hawaiians often want to make things *pono* (good) or *pololei* (correct). To that end, I contacted noted Maui *kumu* Keli'i Tau'a and asked him if he could bless our plants and welcome the long-absent seedlings back into the *ahupua'a* of Auwahi. Keli'i Tau'a has been present at the beginnings of great projects before. He had been there with the double-hulled voyaging canoes, first the *Hōkūle'a* and then its great twin, the *Hawai'iloa*. It was Keli'i who, when winds had failed, went down to the Society Islands to chant for winds—and winds had followed. Keli'i Tau'a has taught for years at Baldwin High School, in Kahului, Maui, a truly loved teacher and mentor for Hawaiian music, dance, and culture.

The morning of the blessing was a typical one at 'Ulupalakua, calm and clear and quiet, save for the sound of chickens and the occasional far-off barking of a dog. Our group of twenty to thirty gathered at the greenhouse where Kumu Tau'a, Bully Kapahulehua, and Kapono Kamaunu began the ceremony with *pule* (prayers) and spontaneous words of inspiration. Kumu Tau'a then mixed *'awa* in a heavy wooden bowl that Māhealani Kai'aokamālie carried as he sprinkled the 'awa-water mix around the greenhouse and plants, and as is Hawaiian tradition, paying special attention to the entrance of the structure. With this first part of the blessing completed, the seedlings, planted in forester's dibble tubes and arranged in groups of ninety-eight in black plastic racks, were loaded into pickup trucks for the forty-five-minute uphill drive on rough, rutted ranch roads to their new home.

The group reconvened in Auwahi, at Pu'u 'Ōuli, perched 4,000 feet above the ruffled and slate-blue Pacific. As an essential and tangible representation of the blessing, we gathered to plant a *maile lauli'i* vine within the exclosure. At the trucks, Kumu Tau'a asked how many *maile* we had time to plant. I knew we were coming precariously close to the arrival of the helicopter to sling-load the seedlings to strategically selected sites within the exclosure. I asked Kumu Tau'a if it was okay to plant just one, to which he nodded. To be on the safe side, I grabbed two dibble tubes of *maile lauli'i*, and we headed off.

Single-file, the group wound down the narrow ridge and into our fenced exclosure, gathering and reassembling below a twisted, spreading *kauila* tree, one of only 150 to 200 trees of its kind remaining on Maui. The *kauila* was renowned by Hawaiians for its iron-hard wood and as a symbol of indefatigable strength. It was used in making the very best quality *'ō'ō* (digging sticks), weapons, and *i'e kuku* (*kapa* mallets).

opposite

Wiliwili
Erythrina sandwicensis

Wiliwili, *a summer-deciduous tree, loses its leaves in the summer, at which time it can be seen blooming in brilliant red, salmon, yellow, white, and pale green colors.*
Photo by Masako Cordray

Framed by the rusty-red *liko* (leaf buds) of the *kauila*, Bully Kapahulehua trumpeted the *pū ʻoleʻole* (conch shell) for each of the four cardinal directions. The loud brave cry filled the emptied forest, echoing off its rocky ridges. I found myself wondering how long had it been since the *pū ʻoleʻole* had sounded at Auwahi. One hundred years? Two hundred? Three hundred? More? Maybe that was the reason the dryland forest at Auwahi had fallen on such hard times!

Pieces of *ʻawa* root were added to a bowl with water and massaged. *ʻAwa* don't make seeds anywhere in the Pacific, but are propagated by root and stem cuttings. This means that all *ʻawa* grown and used today are from the very same long-lived plants used by Hawaiians centuries ago. I dug the fair-sized planting hole, not without effort in the rocky ground, laying the *maile* seedling in the hole. Then, without my asking, the second seedling was handed to me, and I put it in the hole next to the first. As I watched the thin, milky *ʻawa* water being poured from the coconut cup into the planting hole, I felt I was watching the *ola* (life) being poured back into the land. I had always thought the *ola* was in the plants, but now I felt the *ola* was in the land itself, awaiting the arrival of the seedlings.

Then Kumu Tauʻa started to *walaʻau* (talk), easily and from the heart. He talked about the spirit having left the land and how we were asking it to return here, to this *ahupuaʻa*, to begin in this exclosure. He said, "You know, up at the truck, I asked Art how many plants to plant and Art said one. I didn't say a word to Art, but two seedlings were brought down and the two were planted right next to each other. This is the Hawaiian way. One for the male side of things, the other for the female side." Then Kumu Tauʻa gave the unnamed hill its name, Mailelua, literally, "the two *maile* vines." From there, Kumu Tauʻa told his feelings and asked for ours. Person after person spoke with eloquence.

For the last ten minutes or so of our *kumu*'s blessing, my eyes were filled with silent tears. I had asked Kumu Tauʻa to give the blessing, but I have to admit I was caught off-guard by its simple power and grace.

Up to that point, the morning had been clear and warm, much like the weather of the previous week and the following week to come. But during the course of the blessing, the skies began to darken. Shortly thereafter, the group clustered on the ridge round the *kauila* tree was engulfed in clouds of rolling *noe* (mist). Then it began to rain—a thin, insistent, white rain that at this elevation quickly changed the warm morning to conditions more favoring hypothermia.

The ensuing helicopter operation to lift the seedlings into the exclosure was almost canceled due to rain and poor visibility. Despite pea-soup conditions, pilot Duke Baldwin said he felt comfortable and that somehow he could see the things he needed to. Seeing Kumu Tau'a at the top of the hill, I said, "Too much rain, *kumu*, too much rain." With his big, warm smile, he cooed, "Very un-Hawaiian, Art, very un-Hawaiian."

The rest of that week, the first week of this new, bright millennium, a crew of about thirty souls planted over 2,000 seedlings of rare Hawaiian dryland species, most of which can grow to thirty to fifty feet. The planting wasn't accomplished without a fight, as the land seemed filled with rocks. But between and beneath these rocks was the blackest, richest loam many of us had ever seen. For species like the rare *'aiea (Nothocestrum)*, after which O'ahu's well-known district is named, probably as many seedlings were planted in one week as there are adult trees in the whole *ahupua'a*. The work went slowly at first, as the *keiki* were so valuable and, after all, many of us barely knew each other at the start. In the beginning of the week, the coordinators all seemed most busy talking, giving instructions for the complicated outplanting procedure. After Wednesday, we didn't need to say a word; everyone knew what we were doing and what came next. By Thursday, the group had become of one mind, working almost silently, except for the occasional ring of a pick on rock. At lunch, words of hope for the future were the theme; the tide seemed turned. *Pau hana* at week's end, the laughing, joking crew had become friends and colleagues-in-arms. Cresting the immense, rounded *pu'u* (hills) of 'Ulupalakua, far below, the islands of Kaho'olawe and Molokini roil the ocean's surface, appearing adrift in the 'Alalākeiki Channel, orange and *uli* (darkened) with the setting sun. We are smiling. It feels *pono;* the *ola* is back at Auwahi.

GLOSSARY

ahupuaʻa   Hawaiian system of land division that cut the islands into pie-shaped wedges from the mountains to the sea. The *ahupuaʻa* divisions often coincide with watershed boundaries.

ahupuaʻa **management**   Forest management concept embracing native Hawaiian values

akua moʻo   A lizard divinity

aliʻi   Chief, chiefess, ruling class

ʻāpana   Land parcel

ʻaumākua   Family or personal gods

ʻawa   Kava, a narcotic drink used ceremonially

conservation easement   A legal means for providing for preservation of land in perpetuity

endangered species   A plant or animal federally classified under the Endangered Species Act as in immediate danger of extinction throughout all or a significant portion of its range

endemic species   A plant or animal found only in Hawaiʻi

epiphyte   A plant that grows on another plant nonparasitically

hālau hula   A *hula* school

hānai   A foster or adopted child

heiau   A native Hawaiian place of worship, a temple or shrine

hiapo   First-born child

hula kahiko   *Hula* in the ancient style

indigenous species   A plant or animal occurring in Hawaiʻi and elsewhere

kaʻao   A legend or tale

kahakai   Beach, seashore

kahu   Honored attendant or guardian

kahuna   Priest or expert in a field

kai   Sea, sea water

kama'āina   Native-born person

kanaka   Human being, helper

kaona   Hidden meaning, as in Hawaiian poetry

kapu   Taboo or prohibition; "keep out"

kīpuka   Variation or change of form, such as an opening in a forest

ko'olau   Windward sides of the Hawaiian islands

kuahiwi   Mountain or high hill

kuahu   An altar

kualono   Region near the mountaintop; ridge

kula   Plain or field; open country

kumu   Teacher

kupuna   Grandparent, ancestor, relative or close friend of the
   grandparent's generation

limu   General name for underwater plants

lo'i kalo   Taro patch

loina   Rule, custom, principle

makai (ma kai)   In the direction of the sea

mālama Hawai'i   To care for, preserve, and protect Hawai'i

mana   Supernatural or divine power

mauka   In the inland direction, toward the mountain

mele   Song, chant, poem

mesic forest   Moist (not wet) forest containing a diversity of plants
   but with no dense fern understory

mokupuni   Island

mo'olelo   Story, myth, tradition

na'au   Mind, heart, affections

ola   Life, health, well-being

oli   Chant not danced to

pae 'āina   Group of islands, archipelago

piko   Navel; summit

pololei   Straight, correct, proper

pono   Goodness, uprightness, morality

pule   Prayer, blessing, spell

threatened species Any species that is likely to become an endangered species with the foreseeable future throughout all or a significant portion of its range

wala'au To talk, converse

wao akua Forested region below the *wao ma'ukele*, said to be occupied by forest spirits

wao kanaka Forested region seaward of the *wao akua*, frequented by human beings for gathering useful materials

wao koa Koa forest

wao ma'ukele Wet area, located in the rain belt of the island

wao nahele Inland forest region

watershed partnership Voluntary, cooperative partnership between public and private landowners to share expertise and resources and to jointly manage watershed forests across ownership boundaries

CONTRIBUTORS

Alani Apio is a woodcarver, actor, dramatist, visual artist, and currently is employed as a director in community and public relations for a public relations firm. His play *Kamau* toured with Kumu Kahua Theater in 1993 and 1994, and *Kamau A'e*, the second part of the *Kamau* trilogy, was produced by Kumu Kahua in 1997. His poetry has been featured in the *Hawai'i Review*, and his fiction has appeared in *Best of Honolulu Fiction: Stories from the Honolulu Magazine Fiction Contest. Kamau* was excerpted in *'Oiwi: A Native Hawaiian Journal.* His articles on Hawaiian sovereignty, multiculturalism, and race and ethnic relations have appeared in several national publications as well as in the *Honolulu Advertiser.*

J. Stephen Athens is general manager and senior archaeologist for the International Archaeological Research Institute in Honolulu. He has done paleoenvironmental and archeological research in Hawai'i, throughout the Pacific islands, and in South America.

Jan Becket has exhibited his black-and-white photography in the San Francisco bay area, Santa Fe, New Mexico, and Paris, as well as in Hawai'i. His work is in collections at the French National Library, Kamehameha Schools, and the Hawai'i State Foundation on Culture and the Arts, and appears in *He Alo A He Alo: Hawaiian Voices on Sovereignty* (American Friends Service Committee, 1993) and *Sacred Sites, Sacred Rites* (American Indian Community House, 1998). He was co-editor and co-photographer for *Pana O'ahu: Sacred Stones, Sacred Land* (University of Hawai'i Press, 1999). He teaches English and photography at Kamehameha Schools.

Michael G. Buck is administrator of the Hawai'i Division of Forestry and Wildlife (DOFAW). The largest of eight line divisions within the Hawai'i Department of Land and Natural Resources, DOFAW is the largest land management entity in the state, with direct responsibility for approximately 800,000 acres of state-owned trust lands. He has held the position since 1989. In addition to overseeing a staff of about 150 persons, he serves as DLNR's spokesperson on forestry, wildlife, and other natural resource management issues. He serves on numerous national committees concerned with forestry and conservation.

Vickie Caraway is State Botanist for the Hawai'i Division of Forestry and Wildlife. Previously, she was the project coordinator for the Hawai'i office of the Center for Plant Conservation. She also worked for Lyon Arboretum and as supervisor of Foster Botanical Garden.

Richard A. Cooke III has served as artist-in-residence on Moloka'i, teaching environmental awareness for the State Foundation on Culture and the Arts and the State Department of Education. His photography has been published in magazines and in Time-Life's *Wilderness Book Series*. He has undertaken photographic assignments from the National Geographic Society for such books as *Canada's Wilderness Lands, America's Wild and Scenic Rivers,* and *Exploring Valleys of North America*. He is also the author and photographer of *Moloka'i: An Island in Time*.

Masako Cordray makes her home in Ha'iku, Maui. Her photography has been widely exhibited in the Islands. Her video "Voice from the North, The Gwich'in People and the Arctic National Wildlife Refuge" received the Houseman Image Award from the Alaska Conservation Foundation.

Eric Enos was a founder and is now program director of Ka'ala Farm, Inc., a Native Hawaiian cultural education and environmental conservation organization. Under his leadership, Ka'ala has been rediscovering the meaning of ahupua'a and the values embodied within it. Working with community young people, he was responsible for restoring the flow of water to Ka'ala's Cultural Learning Center site in upper Wai'anae Valley and replanting ancient *lo'i kalo* (taro paddies). A practicing artist, he is engaged in many community cultural and environmental restoration projects.

Sam 'Ohukani'ōhi'a Gon III is Director of Science at the Nature Conservancy of Hawai'i. He has worked in Hawaiian conservation for over twenty-five years. He serves on the Department of Land and Natural Resources' steering committee for the Year of the Hawaiian Forest. In February 2003, after nine years of study under Kumu John K. Lake, Dr. Gon underwent the traditional Hawaiian *'ailolo* and *'ūniki hu'elepo* ceremonies and graduated as a *kahuna kākalaleo* (practitioner of chant and protocol).

Gail Hovey is development director of Ka'ala Farm, Inc. She has worked for more than a decade on the Wai'anae Coast, helping to bring resources to community organizations. Before coming to Hawai'i in 1991, she worked as an editor and writer in New York City.

Jack Jeffrey is a biologist for the U.S. Fish and Wildlife Service's Hakalau Forest National Wildlife Refuge and a long-time resident of the island of Hawai'i. He is also one of the state's preeminent photographers of birds. His work has been widely published in such magazines as *Audubon, Smithsonian, Life, Natural History, Birders World, National Wildlife, Pacific Discovery, Defenders of Wildlife, Science, National Park,* and *National Geographic (Canon Endangered Species Series)*. With ornithologist H. Douglas Pratt, he has also co-authored two books on native birds, *Hawai'i's Beautiful Birds* and *A Pocket Guide to Hawai'i's Birds.* He was the recipient of the National Sierra Club Ansel Adams Award for Conservation Photography in 2002 .

Pualani Kanaka'ole Kanahele is, along with her sister, Nālani Kanaka'ole, *kumu hula* of Halau o Kekuhi. A teacher of Hawaiian studies, she has written many books and articles on, and appeared in video productions about, Hawaiian cultural values and practices. Her recent book is *Holo Mai Pele,* published by Pacific Islanders in Communications and the Edith Kanaka'ole Foundation, 2001.

Dennis Kawaharada teaches writing and literature at Kapi'olani Community College. He is the author of *Storied Landscapes: Hawaiian Literature and Place* (1999). "Alive in Story" will also appear in *Crossing Seas: Essays on Multicultural Hawai'i,* an autobiographical collection to be published in spring 2004.

Kapulani Landgraf is a photographer, faculty member at Windward Community College, and graduate of Kamehameha Schools. She earned her BA degree in anthropology from the University of Hawai'i and an MFA degree in visual arts from Vermont College. In 1996, she was awarded an Individual Artist Fellowship in photography from the Hawai'i State Foundation on Culture and the Arts (SFCA). Her photography is featured in the *Nā Wahi Kapu o Maui* (forthcoming from 'Ai Pōhaku Press), *Nā Wahi Pana 'O Ko'olau Poko: Legendary Places of Ko'olau Poko,* and *Hawaiian People Today: Nā Mamo.* Her work has been exhibited in numerous one-person and group exhibitions worldwide and is in the collections of the Honolulu Academy of Arts, the Contemporary Museum, Kamehameha Schools, and the SFCA.

David Liittschwager and Susan Middleton have worked together photographing plants and animals for over fifteen years. Their goal has been to create portraits of the animals and plants on the endangered species list. Their books include *Here Today: A Portrait of Our Vanishing Species, Witness: Endangered Species of North America,* and most recently *Remains of a Rainbow: Rare Plants and Animals of Hawai'i* (in association with the National Geographic Society, Environmental Defense, National Tropical Botanical Garden, and Nature Conservancy of Hawai'i). It includes a foreword by W. S. Merwin.

Hal Lum received a bachelor's degree in fine arts from the University of Hawai'i in 1967 and an MFA in sculpture from San Francisco State in 1972. During the 1980s, he and his wife, Masayo, lived in New York, where he learned commercial photography. For the last several years he has worked as a photographer in Hawai'i, while also producing paintings and drawings. His work in various media has been exhibited widely in Hawai'i and on the mainland.

Art Medeiros has worked as a biologist on Maui, first with Haleakalā National Park; he has been with the U.S. Geological Survey for the past twenty-three years. He is currently engaged in leeward forest restoration projects at 'Auwahi dryland forest on 'Ulupalakua Ranch, Pu'u-o-kali wiliwili forest on the Department of Hawaiian Home Lands, and remnant koa forests in East Maui through the emergent Leeward Haleakalā Watershed Restoration Partnership.

W. S. Merwin has often written of his love and concern for the Islands in his forty volumes of poetry and prose. His many awards include the Pulitzer Prize for Poetry, the Bollingen Prize in Poetry, the Tanning Prize, and the Hawai'i Governor's Award for Literature. A long-time resident of Maui, he has been an active supporter of environmental and social causes.

John Obata is a retired school teacher whose interest in the biological resources of Hawai'i has spanned over five decades. He has served as mentor to many of today's leading field biologists and naturalists.

Rob Pacheco is President and Director of Interpretive Naturalists for Hawai'i Forest and Trail. He also sits on several boards including the Mauna Kea Management Board, TREE (Tropical Reforestation and Ecosystem Education) Center, Big Island Visitors Bureau, the Paniolo Preservation Society, and the Mauna Kea Activities Association.

Anne Nanea Kahiwahiwa Rosa works for the Nature Conservancy's O'ahu program as the Service Learning Coordinator in charge of coordinating field education programs and Project Stewardship, a program for high school students. She has worked as an intern with the Hanauma Bay Education Program, surveying natural and cultural resources of the Waipā Ahupua'a in Waipā, Kaua'i, and as a field intern with the Nature Conservancy of Hawai'i's Honouliuli Preserve.

Franco Salmoiraghi is one of the Islands' most renowned photographers. His photographs have been featured in the books *Eros; Hawai'i; Christmas Island; Change We Must, My Spiritual Journey,* by Nana Veary; *Portfolio Hawai'i: The Big Island;* and *A Day in the Life of Hawai'i.* Recent commissions include photographing Kaho'olawe for the highly acclaimed exhibition *Kaho'olawe: Rebirth of a Sacred Hawaiian Island* and the book *Kaho'olawe: Na Leo o Kanaloa,* and documenting the Ka'ūpūlehu area of the Big Island for the book *In the Lee of Hualalai.* His photographs are in the collections of the Los Angeles County Museum of Art, the New Orleans Museum of Art, the Hawai'i State Foundation on Culture and the Arts, the Honolulu Academy of Arts, and the Contemporary Museum.

Frank Stewart is editor of the Pacific and Asian literary journal *Mānoa*, published by the University of Hawai'i Press. He has edited several books on environmental writing in Hawai'i and elsewhere, including *A World between Waves* and *The Presence of Whales*. He is also the author of *A Natural History of Nature Writing* and numerous environmental essays in books such as *Father Nature: Fathers As Guides to the Natural World* and *Other Oceans*.

Nainoa Thompson is the Executive Director of the Polynesian Voyaging Society. Since 1976 he has played an integral part in the design, construction, sailing, and navigation of the double-hulled voyaging canoe *Hōkūle'a*. In 1980, he navigated *Hōkūle'a* from Hawai'i to Tahiti and back. In 1994 he supervised construction of *Hawai'iloa*, a Hawaiian voyaging canoe built of traditional materials. On its maiden voyage in 1995, the canoe crossed the Pacific from Hawai'i to Tahiti to Ra'iatea, returning via Nuku Hiva.

P. Quentin Tomich settled in Honoka'a in 1959. Educated in medical zoology and ecology at the University of California at Berkeley and Davis, he gained extensive field experience in California, Arctic Alaska, and Egypt. In his twenty-six years at the Hawai'i Department of Health, he engaged in studies of bubonic plague, leptospirosis, rodents, fleas, mongoose, and the Hawaiian hoary bat. He also served for eight years as chair of the state's Natural Area Reserves System Commission and is the author of numerous books and scientific papers. In retirement he works a small farm in Kalopā Homesteads.

Shuzo Uemoto is staff photographer for the Honolulu Academy of Arts and a photography instructor at Kapi'olani Community College. His photographs and prints have been shown in local, national, and international exhibitions and in numerous magazines. His books include *Nana I Na Loea Hula: Look to the Hula Resources*, published by the Kalihi-Palama Culture and Arts Society; and *Lessons of Aloha: Stories of the Human Spirit*, written by Brother Noland with photographs by Shuzo Uemoto.

Jolie Wanger is the Information and Education Specialist for the state's Division of Forestry and Wildlife (DOFAW). She has a B.A. in biology from Boston University and an M.A. in geography from the University of Hawai'i. Her work in conservation has taken her throughout the United States and to Honduras, Mexico, and Bali. Although primarily interested in the marine environment before coming to DOFAW, she has been bewitched by the unique forests of Hawai'i and hopes to help introduce the rest of the *mauka*-shy folks of Hawai'i to their wonders.

ACKNOWLEDGMENTS

This project is dedicated to the inspiring and irreplaceable Hawaiian forests. The project director would like to thank the staff and leadership of the Division of Forestry and Wildlife, state of Hawai'i, for supporting this project, specifically Mike Buck, Randy Kennedy, Ron Cannarella, Vickie Caraway, and Betsy Gagné. Thank you to Barbara Pope and the staff of Barbara Pope Book Design for their dedication, perseverance, and creativity. Also *mahalo* to Pauline Sato and Beth McDermott for their overall support and assistance in making connections with contributors to this book. Last, thank you to the authors and photographers who rose to the task and provided us with such reflective and thought-provoking work from their hearts and experiences.

Funding was provided by the state of Hawai'i's Natural Area Reserve Fund, Ka'ulunani Urban and Community Forestry Program, and a Conservation Education grant from the U.S.D.A. Forest Service.

PERMISSIONS

The following essays and poems have not previously been published and appear here with the kind permission of the authors: Alani Apio, "Giving Back"; Jan Becket, "Land and Literature: Teaching about the Hawaiian Forest"; Michael G. Buck, "Introduction: Rains Always Follow the Forest"; Eric Enos, with Gail Hovey, "Bringing Down the Water"; Sam ʻOhukaniʻōhiʻa Gon III, "Kāhela i Luna ke alo o Lanihuli"; Pualani Kanakaʻole Kanahele, "Native Hawaiian Environment"; Dennis Kawaharada, "Alive in Story"; A. C. Medeiros, "The Puʻolēʻolē Blows and ʻAwa Is Poured"; Anne Nanea Kahiwahiwa Rosa, "Honouliuli"; Jolie R. Wanger, "Sunset at Kaʻala."

The editors gratefully acknowledge permission to reprint the following previously published works:

Vickie Caraway, "Blue Hawaiʻi: Conservation in Paradise," from *Native Plants,* volume 18, number 1, Winter 2001. "Mea Kanu," from *ESA Today,* Winter 2001.

Sam ʻOhukaniʻōhiʻa Gon III, "Think Mauka," from *Honolulu Weekly,* January 1–7, 2003.

Kapulani Landgraf, from *Nā Wahi Kapu O Maui* (Honolulu: Māhoe Mua, 2003).

W. S. Merwin, "Rain at Night," reprinted from *The Rain in the Trees* (Random House, Inc., 1988).

Rob Pacheco, "Inventory of a Koa," reprinted from "Reading the Land: Monthly Essays by Rob Pacheco," Web Site of Hawaiʻi Forest and Trail <www.hawaii-forest.com>, 2002; also in *Growing Koa: A Hawaiian Legacy Tree,* edited by Kim M. Wilkinson and Craig R. Elevitch (Holualoa: Permanent Agriculture Resources, 2003).

Nainoa Thompson, excerpt from "Hawaiʻiloa: 1990–1995: Articles by Nainoa Thompson," Web Site of the Polynesian Voyaging Society <www.pvs-hawaii.org>, 1995; also in *Growing Koa: A Hawaiian Heritage Tree,* edited by Kim M. Wilkinson and Craig R. Elevitch (Holualoa: Permanent Agriculture Resources, 2003).

Quentin Tomich, "The Loulu: Our Native Fan Palms," from *Hamakua Times,* August 1999; "Ōhiʻa: Adventures with a Genetic Marvel" appeared as "Adventures with a Genetic Marvel: The Ōhiʻa Tree," in *Hamakua Times,* February 2000.

Directed by Jolie Wanger, Information and Education Specialist for the Department of Land and Natural Resources, Division of Forestry and Wildlife.

Edited by Frank Stewart, with Jolie Wanger and Barbara Pope.

Copyedited by Ken Banks and Sally Serafim.

Art selected by Barbara Pope, with Jolie Wanger.

Captions written by Jolie Wanger, with assistance from Vickie Caraway, Scott Fretz, and Barbara Pope.

✺

First published in 2003 by the
Division of Forestry and Wildlife
Department of Land and Natural Resources
State of Hawai'i; reprinted in 2004

For information on how to obtain copies of this book, please contact:
Jolie Wanger
Information and Education Specialist
DLNR/Division of Forestry and Wildlife
1151 Punchbowl Street, Room 325
Honolulu, Hawai'i 96813
TEL: (808) 587-4188
E-MAIL: jolie.r.wanger@hawaii.gov

ISBN 1-883528-25-9
LCCN 2003096252

Designed and produced by Barbara Pope Book Design.

Printed in China.